PRIMARY

C000006255

comprehension

Fiction and nonfiction texts

Science Fiction

Poetry

Mystery

Myth/Legend

Fable

Play

Adventure

Fantasy

Fairytale

Horror/Supernatural

Humorous

Published by Prim-Ed Publishing

www.prim-ed.com

6257C

PRIMARY COMPREHENSION *(Book E)*

Published by Prim-Ed Publishing 2006

Reprinted under licence by Prim-Ed Publishing 2006

Copyright© R.I.C. Publications® 2005

ISBN 1 84654 012 7

PR–6257

Additional titles available in this series:
PRIMARY COMPREHENSION *(Book A)*
PRIMARY COMPREHENSION *(Book B)*
PRIMARY COMPREHENSION *(Book C)*
PRIMARY COMPREHENSION *(Book D)*
PRIMARY COMPREHENSION *(Book F)*
PRIMARY COMPREHENSION *(Book G)*

Internet websites

In some cases, websites or specific URLs may be recommended. While these are checked and rechecked at the time of publication, the publisher has no control over any subsequent changes which may be made to webpages. It is *strongly* recommended that the class teacher checks *all* URLs before allowing students to access them.

View all pages online

Website: www.prim-ed.com
Email: sales@prim-ed.com

PRIMARY COMPREHENSION

Foreword

Primary comprehension is a series of seven books designed to provide opportunities for pupils to read texts in a variety of fiction, poetry and nonfiction genres, to answer questions at literal, deductive and evaluative levels and to practise a variety of selected comprehension strategies.

Titles in this series include:

- *Primary Comprehension* Book A
- *Primary Comprehension* Book B
- *Primary Comprehension* Book C
- *Primary Comprehension* Book D
- *Primary Comprehension* Book E
- *Primary Comprehension* Book F
- *Primary Comprehension* Book G

Contents

TEACHERS NOTES

Twenty different texts from a variety of genres are given. These include humour, fantasy, a myth/legend, folktale, mystery, adventure, horror/supernatural, fairytale, play, fable, science fiction, poetry and informational texts/nonfiction such as a timetable, letter, report, procedure, poster, map, programme, book cover and cartoon.

Three levels of questions are used to indicate the reader's comprehension of each text.

One or more particular comprehension strategies has been chosen for practice with each text.

Each text is given over four pages. Each group of four pages consists of:

~ a teachers page

~ pupil page – 1   (which always includes the text and sometimes literal questions)

~ pupil page – 2   (which gives literal, deductive and evaluative questions)

~ pupil page – 3   (which concentrates on the chosen comprehension strategy/ strategies)

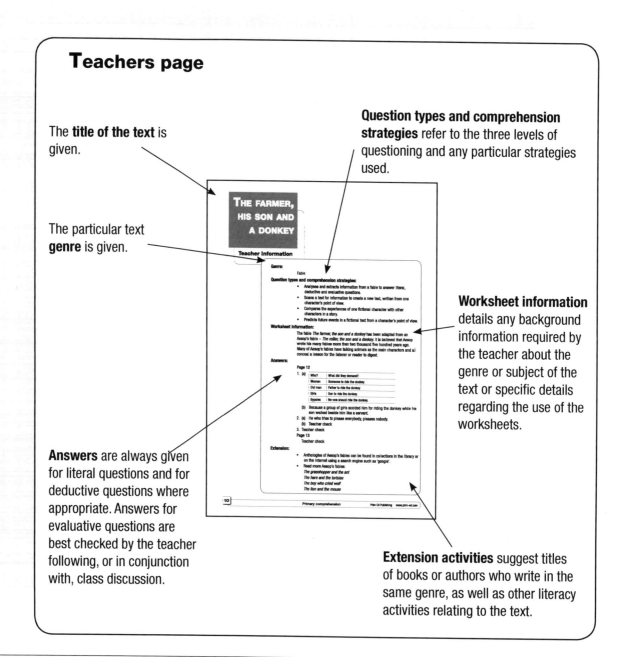

Teachers page

The **title of the text** is given.

Question types and comprehension strategies refer to the three levels of questioning and any particular strategies used.

The particular text **genre** is given.

Worksheet information details any background information required by the teacher about the genre or subject of the text or specific details regarding the use of the worksheets.

Answers are always given for literal questions and for deductive questions where appropriate. Answers for evaluative questions are best checked by the teacher following, or in conjunction with, class discussion.

Extension activities suggest titles of books or authors who write in the same genre, as well as other literacy activities relating to the text.

TEACHERS NOTES

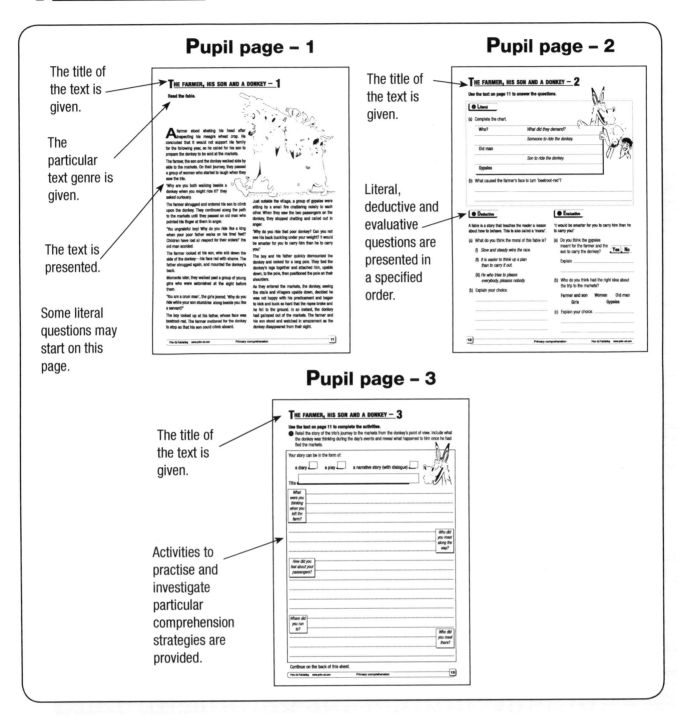

Pupil page – 1

The title of the text is given.

The particular text genre is given.

The text is presented.

Some literal questions may start on this page.

Pupil page – 2

The title of the text is given.

Literal, deductive and evaluative questions are presented in a specified order.

Pupil page – 3

The title of the text is given.

Activities to practise and investigate particular comprehension strategies are provided.

Types of questions

Pupils are given **three types (or levels) of questions** to assess their comprehension of a particular text in each genre:

- **Literal questions** are those which can be found directly in the text. These come first in the questions and are grouped.
- **Deductive (or inferential) questions** follow the literal questions. Deductive questions are implied in the text and require the reader to read between the lines and think a bit more deeply about what has just been read.
- **Evaluative (or response/applied) questions** require the reader to think even further about the text and incorporate his/her personal experiences and knowledge to answer.

Answers for literal questions are always given and may be found on the teachers page. Answers for deductive questions are given where appropriate. Evaluative questions are best checked by the teacher following, or in conjunction with, class discussion.

Comprehension strategies

Reading comprehension is an essential part of the reading process. Pupils need to comprehend what they read in order to become fluent readers.

The teacher is crucial in teaching and encouraging the use of comprehension strategies. Pupils' comprehension improves when teachers provide explicit instruction in comprehension strategies and when they implement activities that provide opportunities to practise and understand these strategies.

Several specific comprehension strategies have been selected for practice in this book.

Although specific examples have been selected, often other strategies, such as scanning, are used in conjunction with those indicated, even though they may not be stated. Rarely does a reader use a single strategy to comprehend a text.

Strategy definitions

Predicting

Prediction involves the pupils using illustrations, text or background knowledge to help them construct meaning. Pupils might predict what texts could be about, what could happen or how characters could act or react. Prediction may occur before, during and after reading, and can be adjusted during reading.

Pages 2–5, 6–9, 10–13, 14–17, 42–45 and 62–65 use the strategy of predicting.

Making connections

Pupils comprehend texts by linking their prior knowledge and the new information given in the text. Pupils may make connections between the text and themselves, between the new text and other texts previously read, and between the text and the world.

Pages 14–17, 18–21, 22–25, 26–29, 34–37, 58–61 and 70–73 use the strategy of making connections.

Comparing

This strategy is closely linked to the strategy of making connections. Pupils make comparisons by thinking more specifically about the similarities and differences between the connections being made.

Pages 2–5, 10–13, 30–33, 34–37 and 54–57 use the strategy of comparing.

Sensory imaging

Sensory imaging involves pupils utilising all five senses to create mental images of passages in the text. Pupils use visual, auditory, olfactory, kinaesthetic or emotional images as well as their personal experiences to create these images. The images may help them to make predictions, form conclusions, interpret information and remember details.

Pages 38–41, 42–45 and 46–49 use the strategy of sensory imaging.

Determining importance

The strategy of determining importance is particularly helpful when pupils are trying to comprehend informational texts. It involves pupils determining the important theme or main idea of particular paragraphs or passages.

As pupils become effective readers, they will constantly ask themselves what is most important in a phrase, sentence, paragraph, chapter or whole text. To determine importance, pupils will need to use a variety of information, such as the purpose for reading, their knowledge of the topic, background experiences and beliefs, and understanding of the text format.

Pages 46–49, 50–53 and 78–81 use the strategy of determining importance.

TEACHERS NOTES

Skimming	Skimming is the strategy of looking quickly through texts to gain a general impression or overview of the content. Readers often use this strategy to quickly assess whether a text, or part of it, will meet their purpose. Because this book deals predominantly with comprehension *after* reading, skimming has not been included as one of the major strategies.
Scanning	Scanning is the strategy of quickly locating specific details such as dates, places or names, or those parts of the text which support a particular point of view. Scanning is often used but not specifically mentioned when used in conjunction with other strategies.
	Pages 10–13, 34–37, 54–57, 58–61, 62–65 and 74–77 use the strategy of scanning.
Synthesising	Synthesising is the strategy which enables pupils to collate a range of information from a variety of sources in order to comprehend texts. Pupils recall information, order details and piece information together to make sense of the texts. Synthesising helps pupils to continually monitor their understanding of the text. Synthesising involves connecting, comparing, determining importance, posing questions and creating images.
	Pages 18–21, 30–33, 66–69 and 70–73 use the strategy of synthesising.

Paraphrasing/Summarising

Summarising involves the processes of recording key ideas, main points or the most important information from a text. Summarising or paraphrasing reduces a larger piece of text to the most important details.

Pages 22–25, 50–53, 66–69, 70–73, 74–77 and 78–81 use the strategy of summarising/paraphrasing.

Shared and guided reading

Reading comprehension needs to be taught if pupils are to learn how to understand and engage with texts. The structure of comprehension lessons needs to provide direct teaching on the application of reading comprehension strategies.

Shared reading	To introduce the lesson, the teacher models reading the text, including a demonstration of how to use the comprehension strategies required by the specific unit of work. The demonstration might include: • linking information in new text to prior knowledge • generating mental images of parts of text • asking 'why' questions • pausing during reading and asking predictive questions or any of the strategies outlined on pages vi and vii.
Guided reading	The pupils work in groups to complete the comprehension activities. The teacher works with and supports the pupils, prompting them to use different strategies to solve the questions; for example, the strategy modelled in the shared reading session should be applied to the text.
Plenary	Comprehension lessons should be concluded using a plenary session, giving the teacher and pupils the opportunity to discuss a range of issues, including: • re-emphasis and practise of strategies • clarification of misconceptions • reflection and personal response • explanation of how pupils solved particular questions • presentation and discussion of work

TEACHERS NOTES

Genre definitions

Fiction and poetry

Science fiction
These stories include backgrounds or plots based upon possible technology or inventions, experimental medicine, life in the future, environments drastically changed, alien races, space travel, gene engineering, dimensional portals or changed scientific principles. Science fiction encourages readers to suspend some of their disbelief and examine alternate possibilities.

Horror/Supernatural
Stories of this type are those which aim to make the reader feel fear, disgust or horror. A number of horror stories have become classics. These include *Frankenstein* by Mary Shelley, *Dracula* by Bram Stoker and *Dr Jekyll and Mr Hyde* by Robert Louis Stevenson.

Mystery stories
Stories of this kind focus on suspense and the solving of a mystery. Plots of mysteries often revolve around a crime, such as murder, theft or kidnapping. The hero must solve the mystery, overcoming unusual events, threats, assaults and often unknown forces or enemies. Stories about detectives, police, private investigators, amateur sleuths, spies, thrillers and courtroom dramas usually fall into this genre.

Fables
A fable is a short story which states a moral. Fables often use talking animals or animated objects as the main characters. The interaction of the animals or animated objects reveals general truths about human nature.

Fairytales
These tales are usually about elves, dragons, hobgoblins, sprites or magical beings and are often set in the distant past. Fairytales usually begin with the phrase 'Once upon a time ...' and end with the words ' ... and they lived happily ever after'. Charms, disguises and talking animals may also appear in fairytales.

Fantasy
A fantasy may be any text or story which is removed from reality. Stories may be set in nonexistent worlds such as an elf kingdom, on another planet or in alternate versions of the known world. The characters may not be human (dragons, trolls etc.) or may be humans who interact with non-human characters.

Folktales
Stories which have been passed from one generation to the next by word of mouth rather than being written down are folktales. Folktales may include sayings, superstitions, social rituals, legends or lore about the weather, animals or plants.

Plays
Plays are specific pieces of drama, usually enacted on a stage by a number of actors dressed in make-up and appropriate costumes.

Adventure stories
Exciting events and actions feature in these stories. Character development, themes or symbolism are not as important as the actions or events in an adventure story.

Humour
Humour involves characters or events which promote laughter, pleasure or humour in the reader.

Poetry
This is a genre which utilises rhythmic patterns of language. The patterns include meter (high and low stressed syllables), syllabification (the number of syllables in each line), rhyme, alliteration, or a combination of these. Poems often use figurative language.

Myths
These are stories which explain a belief, practice or natural phenomenon and usually involve gods, demons or supernatural beings. A myth does not necessarily have a basis in fact or a natural explanation.

Legends
Legends are told as though the events were actual historical events. Legends may or may not be based on an elaborated version of an historical event. Legends are usually about human beings, although gods may intervene in some way throughout the story.

Genre definitions

Nonfiction

Reports
Reports are written documents describing the findings of an individual or group. They may take the form of a newspaper report, sports or police report, or a report about an animal, person or object.

Biographies
An account of a person's life written by another person is a biography. The biography may be about the life of a celebrity or a historical figure.

Reviews
A review is a concise summary or critical evaluation of a text, event, object or phenomenon. A review may give a perspective, argument or purpose. It offers critical assessment of content, effectiveness, noteworthy features and often ends with a suggestion of audience appreciation.

Letters
These are written conversations sent from one person to another. Letters usually begin with a greeting, contain the information to be related and conclude with a farewell signed by the sender.

Procedures
Procedures are instructions which tell how to make or do something. They use clear, concise language and command verbs. A list of materials required to complete the procedure is included and the instructions are set out in easy-to-follow steps.

Diaries
A diary contains a description of daily events in a person's life.

Other **informational texts** such as **timetables** are excellent sources to teach and assess comprehension skills. Highly visual texts such as diagrams have been included because they provide the reader with other comprehension cues and are less reliant on word recognition.

CURRICULUM LINKS

England   Literacy Year 5

Texts

Legend of text columns (title — pages):
1. A long way from home — Pages 2–5
2. The babysitter's revenge — Pages 6–9
3. The farmer, his son and a donkey — Pages 10–13
4. Sarah and the secret castle — Pages 14–17
5. The great race — Pages 18–21
6. The dolphin mystery — Pages 22–25
7. Bowey Island — Pages 26–29
8. Bakerstown Council — Pages 30–33
9. The troll/Different — Pages 34–37
10. The giant with teeth of fire — Pages 38–41
11. Stop clowning around! — Pages 42–45
12. The saltcellar trick — Pages 46–49
13. Superstitious — Pages 50–53
14. Cinema situation — Pages 54–57
15. Leonardo da Vinci — Pages 58–61
16. The painting in the shed — Pages 62–65
17. Blaze destroys school — Pages 66–69
18. The first spider — Pages 70–73
19. Firstborn fury — Pages 74–77
20. Change your life! — Pages 78–81

Objectives

Term 1

Objective	1	2	3	4	5	6	7	8	9	10	11	12	13	14	15	16	17	18	19	20
Read a range of fiction and poetry:																				
– playscripts													•							
Read a range of nonfiction:																				
– recounts	•														•					
– news reports																•	•			
– instructional texts												•								
Text level work:																				
– investigate how characters are presented		•		•	•	•	•				•									•
– understand dramatic conventions													•							
– analyse and compare poems									•											
– develop an active attitude towards reading		•	•	•	•	•	•			•	•							•		•
– write playscripts													•							
– identify features of recounted texts	•															•	•	•		
– read range of instructional texts												•								
– write instructional texts												•								
– make notes for different purposes	•															•				

Term 2

Objective	1	2	3	4	5	6	7	8	9	10	11	12	13	14	15	16	17	18	19	20
Read a range of fiction and poetry:																				
– traditional stories from a range of cultures									•											
– myths																		•		
– fables			•																	
Read a range of nonfiction:																				
– reports																•	•			
Text level work:																				
– identify the features of myths and fables			•															•		
– investigate the features of different fiction genres		•	•	•	•	•	•			•	•							•		•
– write own versions of fables			•																	
– locate information through skimming, scanning and close reading																•	•			
– compose non-chronological reports																	•			

CURRICULUM LINKS

England Literacy Year 5

Texts (by page range):

#	Text	Pages
1	A long way from home	2–5
2	The babysitter's revenge	6–9
3	The farmer, his son and a donkey	10–13
4	Sarah and the secret castle	14–17
5	The great race	18–21
6	The dolphin mystery	22–25
7	Bowey Island	26–29
8	Bakerstown Council	30–33
9	The troll/Different	34–37
10	The giant with teeth of fire	38–41
11	Stop clowning around!	42–45
12	The saltcellar trick	46–49
13	Superstitious	50–53
14	Cinema situation	54–57
15	Leonardo da Vinci	58–61
16	The painting in the shed	62–65
17	Blaze destroys school	66–69
18	The first spider	70–73
19	Firstborn fury	74–77
20	Change your life!	78–81

Objectives — Term 3

Objective	1	2	3	4	5	6	7	8	9	10	11	12	13	14	15	16	17	18	19	20
Read a range of fiction and poetry:																				
– stories from a variety of cultures										●										
Read a range of nonfiction:																				
– persuasive writing								●						●					●	
Text level work:																				
– investigate texts from different cultures										●										
– explore the appeal of older literature										●										
– read and evaluate letters								●						●						
– read other persuasive texts																			●	
– evaluate texts for persuasiveness								●						●					●	
– collect use of persuasive devices								●												
– write letters								●												
– construct argument in note form to persuade others of a point of view																			●	

Northern Ireland English (Reading) Year 6

Category	Objective	1	2	3	4	5	6	7	8	9	10	11	12	13	14	15	16	17	18	19	20
Range	engage with a range of texts, including:																				
	– stories	●	●	●	●	●	●	●			●	●							●		●
	– poems										●										
	– plays												●								
	– informational material								●					●	●	●	●	●		●	
Purpose	read for information	●	●	●	●	●	●	●	●	●	●	●	●	●	●	●	●	●	●	●	●
	acquire skills necessary to locate information within texts	●	●	●	●	●	●	●	●	●	●	●	●	●	●	●	●	●	●	●	●
Reading activities	participate in shared reading	●	●	●	●	●	●	●	●	●	●	●	●	●	●	●	●	●	●	●	●
	discussing/interpreting texts	●	●	●	●	●	●	●	●	●	●	●	●	●	●	●	●	●	●	●	●
	represent texts in a range of visual forms and diagrams	●		●		●	●	●			●	●		●	●			●		●	●
	justify responses using inference, deduction and reference to evidence in text	●	●	●	●	●	●	●	●		●	●	●	●	●	●	●	●	●	●	●
	consider aspects of stories	●	●	●	●	●	●	●			●	●							●		●
Expected outcomes	respond with sensitivity	●	●			●	●	●	●	●	●	●			●				●	●	
	discuss intentions of writer		●						●	●					●					●	
	extend range of their reading	●	●	●	●	●	●	●	●	●	●	●	●	●	●	●	●	●	●	●	●
	use variety of reading skills for different reading purposes	●	●	●	●	●	●	●	●	●	●	●	●	●	●	●	●	●	●	●	●

CURRICULUM LINKS

Northern Ireland
English (Reading)
Year 6

Texts

Objectives		A long way from home (Pages 2–5)	The babysitter's revenge (Pages 6–9)	The farmer, his son and a donkey (Pages 10–13)	Sarah and the secret castle (Pages 14–17)	The great race (Pages 18–21)	The dolphin mystery (Pages 22–25)	Bowey Island (Pages 26–29)	Bakerstown Council (Pages 30–33)	The troll/Different (Pages 34–37)	The giant with teeth of fire (Pages 38–41)	Stop clowning around! (Pages 42–45)	The saltcellar trick (Pages 46–49)	Superstitious (Pages 50–53)	Cinema situation (Pages 54–57)	Leonardo da Vinci (Pages 58–61)	The painting in the shed (Pages 62–65)	Blaze destroys school (Pages 66–69)	The first spider (Pages 70–73)	Firstborn fury (Pages 74–77)	Change your life! (Pages 78–81)
Expected outcomes	place themselves in someone else's position and extend their capacity for sympathy and empathy	●	●		●	●	●		●		●	●			●		●	●	●	●	●
	speculate on situations read about, predict what may happen or consider what might have happened had circumstances been different	●	●	●	●		●					●					●		●		●
	model their own writing on the forms encountered in their reading		●	●		●		●	●		●		●	●		●	●	●		●	●

Republic of Ireland   English Language (Reading/Writing) 4th Class

Receptiveness to language	use reading as a stimulus to writing	●	●	●	●	●	●	●	●	●	●	●	●	●	●	●	●	●	●	●	●
Competence and confidence	experience different types of text	●	●	●	●	●	●	●	●	●	●	●	●	●	●	●	●	●	●	●	●
	engage with variety of poetry										●										
	develop information retrieval skills	●	●	●	●	●	●	●	●	●	●	●	●	●	●	●	●	●	●	●	●
Developing cognitive abilities	continue to develop a range of comprehension strategies	●	●	●	●	●	●	●	●	●	●	●	●	●	●	●	●	●	●	●	●
	write in a variety of genres	●	●	●	●	●	●	●	●			●		●			●	●		●	●
	summarise text			●			●						●	●			●	●	●		●
	write directions on how to perform a particular process												●								
	write a list of questions							●		●							●				
Emotional and imaginative development	respond to increasingly challenging reading material	●	●	●	●	●	●	●	●	●	●	●	●	●	●	●	●	●	●	●	●

Scotland   English Language (Reading)   Primary 6

Level C																					
Reading for information:	scan for specific information	●	●	●	●	●	●	●	●	●	●	●	●	●	●	●	●	●	●	●	●
	identify the sequence of information in texts			●							●		●	●			●				●
	record information in different ways	●	●	●	●	●	●	●	●	●	●	●	●	●	●	●	●	●	●	●	●
Reading for enjoyment:	identify with characters, comment on their behaviour/reasons and compare to own experiences	●	●		●	●	●		●		●	●	●		●			●	●	●	●
Reading to reflect on the writer's ideas and craft:	make predictions	●	●	●	●		●					●					●	●	●		●
	identify main ideas	●	●	●	●	●	●	●	●	●	●	●	●	●	●	●	●	●	●	●	●

CURRICULUM LINKS

Scotland
English Language (Reading)
Primary 6

Texts

Objectives	A long way from home (Pages 2–5)	The babysitter's revenge (Pages 6–9)	The farmer, his son and a donkey (Pages 10–13)	Sarah and the secret castle (Pages 14–17)	The great race (Pages 18–21)	The dolphin mystery (Pages 22–25)	Bowey Island (Pages 26–29)	Bakerstown Council (Pages 30–33)	The troll/Different (Pages 34–37)	The giant with teeth of fire (Pages 38–41)	Stop clowning around! (Pages 42–45)	The saltcellar trick (Pages 46–49)	Superstitious (Pages 50–53)	Cinema situation (Pages 54–57)	Leonardo da Vinci (Pages 58–61)	The painting in the shed (Pages 62–65)	Blaze destroys school (Pages 66–69)	The first spider (Pages 70–73)	Firstborn fury (Pages 74–77)	Change your life! (Pages 78–81)
Level C																				
– skim and scan to verify decisions	●	●	●	●	●	●	●	●	●	●	●	●	●	●	●	●	●	●	●	●
– go beyond literal answers to make inferences and conclusions	●	●	●	●	●	●	●	●	●	●	●	●	●	●	●	●	●	●	●	●
• Awareness of genre:																				
– adjust reading approaches to the different ways information is presented in different nonfiction texts								●					●		●	●	●		●	
Level D																				
• Reading for information:																				
– complete practical reading tasks								●					●		●				●	
– gather information from a wide range of formats	●	●	●	●	●	●	●	●	●	●	●	●	●	●	●	●	●	●	●	●
• Reading for enjoyment:																				
– become familiar with features of nonfiction texts								●					●		●	●	●		●	
• Reading to reflect on the writer's ideas and craft:																				
– study characters, events, conflicts etc.	●	●		●	●	●	●		●	●	●			●		●	●	●		
– make predictions	●	●	●	●	●		●				●					●	●	●		
• Awareness of genre:																				
– compare texts		●	●		●			●	●	●			●			●	●		●	●
– recognise how informational texts differ								●					●		●	●	●		●	
– sequence and predict informational texts												●				●	●			
• Knowledge about language:																				
– consider theme, character, relationships, setting and motives	●	●	●	●	●	●	●	●	●	●	●	●		●			●	●	●	
– use terms fact and opinion															●				●	
Level E																				
• Reading for enjoyment:																				
– read a variety of texts	●	●	●	●	●	●	●	●	●	●	●	●	●	●	●	●	●	●	●	●
• Reading to reflect on the writer's ideas and craft:																				
– use previous knowledge and skills to predict content	●	●	●	●		●					●					●	●	●		●
– locate main points of text	●	●	●	●	●	●	●	●	●	●	●	●	●	●	●	●	●	●	●	●
– compare text to own ideas, feelings and opinions	●			●	●	●	●	●	●			●	●	●	●	●	●	●	●	
– evaluate, infer and make judgements	●	●	●	●	●	●	●	●	●	●	●	●	●	●	●	●	●	●	●	●
– think about audience and writer's purpose								●	●	●			●		●				●	●
• Awareness of genre:																				
– compare similarities and differences between texts								●	●			●								

CURRICULUM LINKS

Wales
English (Reading)
Year 5

Texts →

Objectives		A long way from home (2–5)	The babysitter's revenge (6–9)	The farmer, his son and a donkey (10–13)	Sarah and the secret castle (14–17)	The great race (18–21)	The dolphin mystery (22–25)	Bowey Island (26–29)	Bakerstown Council (30–33)	The troll/Different (34–37)	The giant with teeth of fire (38–41)	Stop clowning around! (42–45)	The saltcellar trick (46–49)	Superstitious (50–53)	Cinema situation (54–57)	Leonardo da Vinci (58–61)	The painting in the shed (62–65)	Blaze destroys school (66–69)	The first spider (70–73)	Firstborn fury (74–77)	Change your life! (78–81)
Range:	– develop as independent and reflective readers	•	•	•	•	•	•	•	•	•	•	•	•	•	•	•	•	•	•	•	•
	– read for information, using progressively more challenging texts	•	•	•	•	•	•	•	•	•	•	•	•	•	•	•	•	•	•	•	•
	– read playscripts													•							
	– read and use a wide range of nonfiction sources of information								•				•			•	•	•		•	
	– read texts with challenging subject matter that extends thinking			•		•	•		•	•			•			•	•	•	•	•	
	– read texts with a variety of structural and organisational features	•							•	•			•			•	•	•		•	
	– read modern poetry									•											
	– read texts drawn from a variety of cultures and traditions			•							•								•		
	– read myths, legends and traditional stories			•							•								•		
Skills:	– respond imaginatively to plot, characters, ideas, vocabulary and language in literature	•	•		•	•	•	•		•	•	•		•		•	•	•	•	•	•
	– use inference and deduction and refer to relevant passages to support their opinions	•	•	•	•	•	•	•	•	•	•	•	•	•	•	•	•	•	•	•	•
	– use prediction	•	•	•	•		•					•					•	•	•	•	
	– read for different purposes, including skimming, scanning and detailed reading	•	•	•	•	•	•	•	•	•	•	•	•	•	•	•	•	•	•	•	•
	– pose questions				•		•								•						
	– distinguish between fact and opinion														•					•	
	– consider an argument								•							•				•	
	– make succinct notes	•													•						
	– re-present information in different forms		•	•		•	•	•			•	•		•		•	•			•	•
Language development:	– recognise the organisational, structural and presentational features of different types of text	•			•	•			•	•			•		•	•	•	•		•	•

A LONG WAY FROM HOME

Teacher information

Genre:

Diary entries

Question types and comprehension strategies:

- Analyses and extracts information from diary entries to answer literal, deductive and evaluative questions.
- Makes predictions about a character in a text to create dialogue.
- Compares the advantages and disadvantages of two different settings.

Worksheet information:

Teachers may wish to set the scene before reading the diary entries with the class. Ask the pupils if they can imagine what it would feel like to not only go to a new school, but move hundreds of kilometres away from their family into a dormitory that houses hundreds of children.

Answers:

Page 4

1. (a) A school uniform and sports gear. His mother also bought him new clothes.

   (b) If someone from his home town was going to Gilson Grammar also.

   (c) He would like to stand out among the other children. He used to be the fastest runner at his old school.

   (d) Luke asks his mother to make him cakes and biscuits because the food at the school is inedible. He shares the treats.

2. Teacher check

3. (a) Teacher check

   (b) Answers will vary but may include that Luke will go back to the country and become a farmer or farmhand like his Dad.

Page 5

Teacher check

Extension:

- Pupils imagine they are Luke and write a letter home describing life at the school.
- Imagine that 10 years have passed. Luke writes a letter to Yong in Vietnam describing the last five years of his life since he left school.
- Hold a discussion regarding how Luke should respond to the person who locked him in the toilets. In pairs, pupils write an 'action plan', detailing how to deal with people who bully.

A LONG WAY FROM HOME – 1

Read the diary entries.

This diary belongs to ... Luke Curtin.   KEEP OUT!

Saturday 17

Five hours getting dragged through the shops by Mum is not my idea of fun! I thought once the school uniform and sports gear were bought that we would leave, but Mum decided I needed lots of new 'city clothes' as well! Ugh!

Tomorrow we are heading to the dormitories to see where I am going to live for the next five years! I just wish someone else from home was going to Gilson Grammar School too.

Monday 19

I'm sharing a room with a boy called Yong from Vietnam. His family are paying for him to study here, but eventually, he will go home and be a doctor! (I guess we have something in common, as we both know what we are going to be when we go home.)

Today was all timetables, bells and being shoved around by hundreds of kids. Pretty strange considering I've come from a school with 63 kids in it! I don't see how the teachers are ever going to remember my name!

Tuesday 20

Three days and I haven't seen anything edible in the dinner hall yet. Have called Mum and asked her to post me some homemade cakes and biscuits so I don't fade away. What I would give for some fresh scrambled eggs for breakfast—really yellow eggs—straight from the farm!

MUM'S BISCUITS

Today was our first athletics training. At home, I'm the fastest runner in the school. Here, I'm just one of the new kids from the country. I'm going to have to work hard to show them I'm fast!

Wednesday 21

Not a good day! One of the older kids locked me in the toilet and called me 'farm boy'. Everyone was laughing. I wasn't!

Thursday 22

Mum's cakes and biscuits arrived today. I made a lot of new friends. We shared them in the common room.

Friday 23

My first week is over! Tomorrow morning, after practice, we are allowed to go down to the beach for a swim, then Yong and I are going to go to the video arcade to play games. (Certainly beats helping Dad feed the sheep!)

A LONG WAY FROM HOME – 2

Use the text on page 3 to answer the questions.

❶ Literal

(a) What did Luke need before he started at his new school?

_____

_____

(b) What would make Luke feel better about going to his new school?

_____

_____

(c) Why does Luke decide he will need to work hard at athletics?

_____

_____

(d) What helps Luke to make new friends at the school?

_____

_____

❷ Deductive

(a) How do you think Luke felt when he was locked in the toilet? Write some words or phrases to describe how he felt.

(b) Why do you think Luke feels as though the teachers will never learn his name?

_____

_____

_____

_____

❸ Evaluative

(a) How do you think Luke's feelings about moving to the city and going to a new school have changed by the end of the first week?

MUM'S BISCUITS

_____

_____

(b) Luke mentions in his diary that Yong is going to be a doctor when he goes home. What do you think Luke will be when he goes back to the country?

_____

_____

A LONG WAY FROM HOME – 3

Use the text on page 3 to complete the activities.

Luke's life has changed dramatically—from living in a small country town with his family to boarding at a large city school.

1 With a partner, discuss what you think the advantages and disadvantages of moving to the city might be for Luke. Record your ideas in note form below.

Advantages	Disadvantages

2 Imagine that Luke has completed his first year at Gilson Grammar. He goes home for the summer holidays and sees one of his old friends who stayed in the country.

Write some dialogue between the two friends. Include questions about what has happened in the past year. Write the friend's name in the boxes below.

Luke: _____

_____

_____

Luke: _____

_____

_____

Luke: _____

_____

_____

Luke: _____

THE BABYSITTER'S REVENGE

Teacher information

Genre:

Humour

Question types and comprehension strategies:

- Analyses and extracts information from a humorous narrative to answer literal, deductive and evaluative questions.
- Makes predictions about a narrative and uses these to plan a role-play.

Worksheet information:

- Once the pupils complete their role-plays, they could use the ideas to write narratives that continue the story of Scott and Kate.

Answers:

Page 8

1. (a) Playing a type of video game where they raced Formula 1 cars through the streets of Japan.

   (b) The last time she babysat them she fell asleep on the settee.

   (c) Scott was given a fairy costume to wear and Kate the wrestler's costume; they had assumed it would be the other way around.

2. (a) Answers may include:

   – the company Meg is creating a web site for is called 'Brats' Costumes. She was referring to the previous behaviour of the children.

   – Meg had a 'mischievous smile' when she was taking her digital camera from her bag.

   (b) Teacher check

   (c) Teacher check

3. Teacher check

Page 9

Teacher check

Extension:

- Read other humorous books by authors like Paul Jennings, Roald Dahl and Andy Griffiths.

Read the humorous narrative.

'Meg! Thanks so much for coming. I'll be home before midnight. Have fun kids!' Their mother skips out the front door, her car keys jingling in her hand.

Only moments before, Kate and Scott had been sitting on the carpet in front of the television, laughing and cheering as they raced their Formula 1 cars through the streets of Japan. When the doorbell rang, both cars had spun out of control and crashed.

Now the siblings are frozen in place and silent, staring up at the woman standing in their doorway. Kate and Scott gulp in unison as they think back to how delighted they had been a month ago when they slipped out of their bedrooms to discover Meg, their babysitter, asleep on the settee.

The children had thought it would be hilarious to 'borrow' Meg's lipstick from her handbag and put it on Ralph, their Rottweiler—returning it with dog hair and slobber on it. Scott had thought it ingenious to tip out Meg's perfume and fill it with water from the toilet while Kate was emptying out Meg's tub of hair wax, replacing it with the lard-like cleaning product kept under the laundry sink.

Suddenly, Meg speaks, making both children jump. 'Let's make a deal, kids. You do a favour for me and I won't tell your mother about the pranks you pulled when I was 'resting my eyes' the last time I babysat you.'

Kate and Scott begin nodding frantically and slight, wry grins appear on their faces as they realise that, once again, they are going to get away with their antics.

'You see … during the day I work in web design.' As both children look confused, Meg explains further. 'Companies ask me to design web sites for them for the Internet. I'm creating one for a company called "Brats Costumes and Accessories" and I need some pictures of kids in these costumes for a web page.'

Meg takes a pink, sparkling fairy costume and a blue and red lycra wrestler's costume out of a paper bag. The children's grins broaden as they realise that the evening is going to be a lot more fun than they had first expected. That is until Meg hands Scott the fairy costume and Kate the wrestling costume. Meg turns away—hiding her mischievous smile from the pair—and takes the digital camera from her bag.

The next day at school, Kate and Scott are sitting at their desks in their separate classrooms. The bell to start the day rings and, as they always do, their teachers walk over to the classroom computers and turn them on. Today though, the school's web page doesn't appear on the screen. Instead, pictures of Kate and Scott in their costumes are fading in and out to the sounds of some loud and rather embarrassing sound effects. The children's classmates notice immediately and run over to the computers. Their laughter begins as small chuckles and grows into hysterical fits. In both classrooms, Kate and Scott are trying desperately to disappear underneath their desks.

THE BABYSITTER'S REVENGE – 2

Use the text on page 7 to answer the questions.

❶ Literal

(a) What were Kate and Scott doing before they realised they were being babysat by Meg?

_____

_____

_____

(b) Why were the children able to play pranks on Meg the last time she babysat them?

_____

_____

_____

(c) Why were Scott and Kate surprised when they were given the costumes to wear?

_____

_____

❷ Deductive

(a) Do you think Meg needed the photographs for a web page she was designing?

| Yes | No |

Look for a clue in the text that tells you she may have been lying.

_____

(b) Write some words and phrases to describe how you think Meg reacted and felt when she discovered that the contents of her handbag had been tampered with.

(c) Do you think that Kate and Scott are normally well-behaved children? Explain your answer.

_____

_____

❸ Evaluative

(a) Do you think Meg will agree to babysit the children again?

_____

(b) Do you think the children deserved to be humiliated in front of their friends? Explain your answer.

_____

THE BABYSITTER'S REVENGE – 3

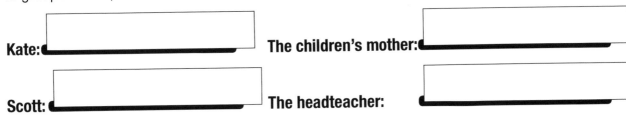

Use the text on page 7 to complete the activities.

Kate, Scott and their mother have been called into the headteacher's office to explain how and why their images now appear on the school's web page.

1 In groups of four, allocate a character to each person in your group.

Kate: _____ The children's mother: _____

Scott: _____ The headteacher: _____

2 Discuss the situation with your group. Make some predictions about what each of the characters will be thinking and saying about the incident.

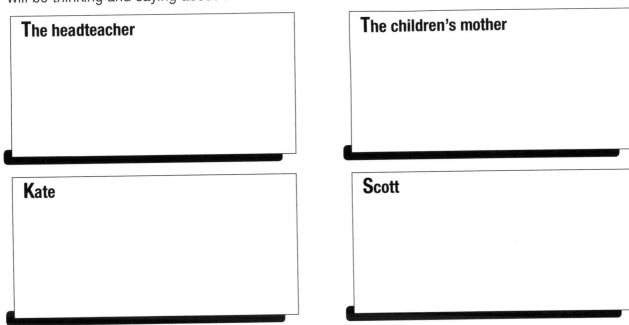

The headteacher

The children's mother

Kate

Scott

3 Plan and present a humorous role-play that takes place in the headteacher's office.

(a) How does the scene start?

_____

_____

_____

_____

(b) How do Scott and Kate explain their images on the school's web page?

_____

_____

_____

(c) How does the scene end? _____

_____

4 Practise your role-play. When you are ready, present it to a small group or the class.

THE FARMER, HIS SON AND A DONKEY

Teacher information

Genre:

Fable

Question types and comprehension strategies:

- Analyses and extracts information from a fable to answer literal, deductive and evaluative questions.
- Scans a text for information to create a new text, written from one character's point of view.
- Compares the experiences of one fictional character with other characters in a story.
- Predicts future events in a fictional text from a character's point of view.

Worksheet information:

The fable *The farmer, the son and a donkey* has been adapted from an Aesop's fable – *The miller, the son and a donkey*. It is believed that Aesop wrote his many fables more than two thousand five hundred years ago. Many of Aesop's fables have talking animals as the main characters and all conceal a lesson for the listener or reader to digest.

Answers:

Page 12

1. (a)

Who?	What did they demand?
Women	Someone to ride the donkey.
Old man	Father to ride the donkey
Girls	Son to ride the donkey.
Gypsies	No-one should ride the donkey.

   (b) Because a group of girls scolded him for riding the donkey while his son walked beside him like a servant.

2. (a) He who tries to please everybody, pleases nobody.
   (b) Teacher check

3. Teacher check

Page 13

Teacher check

Extension:

- Anthologies of Aesop's fables can be found in collections in the library or on the Internet using a search engine such as 'google'.
- Read more Aesop's fables:

  The grasshopper and the ant

  The hare and the tortoise

  The boy who cried wolf

  The lion and the mouse

THE FARMER, HIS SON AND A DONKEY – 1

Read the fable.

A farmer stood shaking his head after inspecting his meagre wheat crop. He concluded that it would not support his family for the following year, so he called for his son to prepare the donkey to be sold at the markets.

The farmer, the son and the donkey walked side by side to the markets. On their journey, they passed a group of women who started to laugh when they saw the trio.

'Why are you both walking beside a donkey when you might ride it?' they asked curiously.

The farmer shrugged and ordered his son to climb upon the donkey. They continued along the path to the markets until they passed an old man who pointed his finger at them in anger.

'You ungrateful boy! Why do you ride like a king when your poor father walks on his tired feet? Children have lost all respect for their elders!' the old man scolded.

The farmer looked at his son, who slid down the side of the donkey—his face red with shame. The father shrugged again, and mounted the donkey's back.

Moments later, they walked past a group of young girls who were astonished at the sight before them.

'You are a cruel man', the girls jeered. 'Why do you ride while your son stumbles along beside you like a servant?'

The boy looked up at his father, whose face was beetroot-red. The farmer motioned for the donkey to stop so that his son could climb aboard.

Just outside the village, a group of gypsies were sitting by a small fire chattering noisily to each other. When they saw the two passengers on the donkey, they stopped chatting and called out in anger.

'Why do you ride that poor donkey? Can you not see his back buckling under your weight? It would be smarter for you to carry him than he to carry you!'

The boy and his father quickly dismounted the donkey and looked for a long pole. They tied the donkey's legs together and attached him, upside down, to the pole, then positioned the pole on their shoulders.

As they entered the markets, the donkey, seeing the stalls and villagers upside down, decided he was not happy with his predicament and began to kick and buck so hard that the ropes broke and he fell to the ground. In an instant, the donkey had galloped out of the markets. The farmer and his son stood and watched in amazement as the donkey disappeared from their sight.

THE FARMER, HIS SON AND A DONKEY – 2

Use the text on page 11 to answer the questions.

❶ Literal

(a) Complete the chart.

Who?	What did they demand?
	Someone to ride the donkey.
Old man	
	Son to ride the donkey.
Gypsies	

(b) What caused the farmer's face to turn 'beetroot-red'?

_____

_____

❷ Deductive

A fable is a story that teaches the reader a lesson about how to behave. This is also called a 'moral'.

(a) What do you think the moral of this fable is?

  (i) *Slow and steady wins the race.*

  (ii) *It is easier to think up a plan than to carry it out.*

  (iii) *He who tries to please everybody, pleases nobody.*

(b) Explain your choice.

_____

_____

_____

❸ Evaluative

'It would be smarter for you to carry him than he to carry you!'

(a) Do you think the gypsies meant for the farmer and the son to carry the donkey? | Yes | No |

Explain _____

_____

(b) Who do you think had the right idea about the trip to the markets?

  Farmer and son   Women   Old man
        Girls   Gypsies

(c) Explain your choice. _____

_____

_____

THE FARMER, HIS SON AND A DONKEY — 3

Use the text on page 11 to complete the activities.

❶ Retell the story of the trio's journey to the markets from the donkey's point of view. Include what the donkey was thinking during the day's events and reveal what happened to him once he had fled the markets.

Your story can be in the form of:

a diary ☐   a play ☐   a narrative story (with dialogue) ☐

Title _____

What were you thinking when you left the farm?

....
....
....

....
....
....

Who did you meet along the way?

How did you feel about your passengers?

....
....
....
....
....

Where did you run to?

....
....

Who did you meet there?

....

Continue on the back of this sheet.

SARAH AND THE SECRET CASTLE

Teacher information

Genre:

Fairytale

Question types and comprehension strategies:

- Analyses and extracts information from a modern-day fairytale to answer literal, deductive and evaluative questions.
- Makes connections between himself/herself and a character from a fictional text.
- Predicts future events in a fictional text from a character's point of view.

Worksheet information:

Prior to reading the text, discuss familiar fairytales. In groups, ask the pupils to discuss the conventions of a fairytale and make a list of what they think the criteria are for a story to be considered a fairytale. (See Teacher notes page viii.)

Answers:

Page 16

1. (a) (i)   a very best friend.

     (ii)   she spotted the long, silver car Josephine disappeared into at the end of each school day outside a block of flats.

     (iii)   exist behind the front door of a shabby, grey flat.

  (b) Possible answers:

    – the butler

    – magnificent ballroom with chandeliers, marble floor and statues

    – servants dusting and polishing

    – Josephine's lavender ball gown and tiara

2. Teacher check

3. Teacher check

Page 17

Teacher check

Extension:

Read other fairytales and fractured fairytales such as:

Snow White in New York by Fiona French

Princess smartypants by Babette Cole

The paper bag princess by Robert Munsch

Revolting rhymes by Roald Dahl

Legally correct fairytales by David Fisher

Read the modern-day fairytale.

Once upon a time, there lived two girls who were in the same class at school. Sarah was quite clumsy but always telling jokes that made her classmates laugh. Josephine was quiet, well-mannered and elegant. Most lunchtimes, both girls could be found in the playground. Josephine would gracefully sit on the swings while Sarah would athletically hang from the monkey bars.

Looking from the outside, the two girls had very little in common. However, there was one thing that they did share—a secret wish to have a very best friend.

One afternoon, Sarah was walking home from her guitar lesson when she spotted the long, silver car Josephine disappeared into at the end of each school day. It was parked outside a block of grey, quite shabby flats. Sarah decided she would see if Josephine wanted to play with her. She tapped on the closest door which was quickly opened by a tall, distinguished looking man wearing a white shirt with a winged collar and tie, a black coat with tails and pinstriped trousers. The man instantly frowned.

'Please go away!' he snapped at Sarah. 'Do not come here again.'

Sarah stared at what she guessed was Josephine's butler. Being the rascal that she was, Sarah ducked down and scrambled into the house through the butler's legs. She quickly stood up and was about to make a run for it to find Josephine but, instead, she froze on the spot! Before her was a magnificent grand ballroom—the size of her school hall! Sarah did a 'double-take', looking back at the front door and then again at the enormous room. It had many chandeliers hanging from its high ceiling, a pristine marble floor and amazing statues that servants were busily dusting and polishing.

Sarah spotted an elegant girl walking down a staircase, wearing a spectacular lavender ball gown. Her hair was piled on top of her head and featured a sparkling tiara.

'You're a princess!' Sarah called out to Josephine, who spun around in her dainty white shoes. Josephine glided over to Sarah and gently pushed her through a marble archway into a room with a dining table the length of a swimming pool!

'How did you …'Josephine began. But then she shook her head and started to whisper. 'You are right. I am a princess. This is my family's castle. You HAVE to promise not to tell. You MUST promise!'

A mischievous smirk spread across Sarah's face. Although her mind was spinning with questions about how a castle could exist behind the front door of a shabby grey flat, Sarah remembered her secret wish.

'I promise I won't tell … but only if you let me play here in the castle with you.'

'OK!' Josephine giggled with excitement, remembering a little too late to politely cover her mouth. 'If you think this room is amazing, wait until you see my bedroom! Oh! And the stables—they're full of ponies!'

Princess Josephine and Sarah made a pact to spend every Saturday afternoon playing together in the castle. And this is exactly what they did. Not long after that, they became the very best of friends.

Sarah and the Secret Castle – 2

Use the text on page 15 to answer the questions.

---

❶ Literal

(a) Complete these sentences.

   (i) Both girls wished they had _____.

   (ii) Sarah discovered where Josephine lived because _____

   _____

   (iii) Sarah was confused about how a castle could _____

   _____

(b) List three things that helped Sarah deduce that Josephine was a princess.

---

❷ Deductive

(a) Write words and phrases to describe how you think Josephine may have felt having to pretend to her classmates that she was an ordinary girl.

(b) Why do you think Josephine made Sarah promise that she wouldn't tell her secret?

_____

_____

_____

❸ Evaluative

(a) Do you think Sarah kept her promise? Explain your answer.

_____

_____

_____

(b) Which character from the story do you most resemble? Tick the traits you have

Sarah: joker ☐   clumsy ☐

          athletic ☐   mischievous ☐

Josephine: graceful ☐   polite ☐

          quiet ☐   proud ☐

(c) On the back of this sheet, draw portraits of Sarah and Josephine. Compare your drawing with a friend's and discuss the similarities and differences.

SARAH AND THE SECRET CASTLE – 3

Use the text on page 15 to help you complete this activity.

1 Sarah had so many questions to ask her new best friend. Write five questions you think she will ask Princess Josephine.

2 Circle one of the questions. Answer it as if you were Princess Josephine.

_____

_____

3 Sarah and Princess Josephine spent so many Saturday afternoons playing together that Sarah's mischievous personality began to 'rub off' on her new best friend.

Choose one of the characters and write a diary entry that describes a Saturday afternoon's adventure.

Character: *Princess Josephine* ☐   *Sarah* ☐

Saturday _____

....

....

....

....

....

....

THE GREAT RACE

Teacher information

Genre:

Fantasy

Question types and comprehension strategies:

- Analyses and extracts information from a fantasy to answer literal, deductive and evaluative questions.
- Synthesises information from a text to create a diary of a character.
- Makes connections between a character in a text and himself/herself to write a personal diary.

Worksheet information:

- Pupils may need assistance in finding information in the text to create Sashoc's diary. Prompt pupils by asking questions such as:
  - What type of environment does Sashoc live in?
  - What types of foods would be found there?
  - What type of training would develop Sashoc's skills so she could jump away from sand suckers and dodge the Flying Ferriers? She also needs to be very fit to complete the long distance race.
  - Would Sashoc travel to Peril Sands alone? Who would she go with?
  - Would she have a vehicle, ride on an animal or walk to Peril Sands?
  - Is Peril Sands very far from the Dodzin Desert?

Answers:

Page 20

1. (a) (i) Peril Sands
       (ii) Sanzoc, a Sand Creature from the Dodzin Desert
       (iii) Flying Ferriers
       (iv) Desert Dopplers
       (v) Sashoc, the great-granddaughter of Sanzoc
2. Teacher check
3. Teacher check

Page 21

Teacher check

Extension:

Read other novels that are set in nonexistent world's such as:

The hobbit by JRR Tolkien

Northern lights by Philip Pullman

Harry Potter series by JK Rowling

Neverending story by Michael Ende

THE GREAT RACE – 1

Read the fantasy story.

Creatures from all over Namboodya have camped out under the Great Star and seven moons, excitedly anticipating the Great Race. It is the highlight of the year for all who inhabit Namboodya. For on this one day, as it has been for hundreds of centuries, all wars cease and all conflicts are put aside.

Peril Sands, the barren stretch of land between the Areill Mountains and the town of Nambi, is the site for the race. Once the moons have disappeared over the mountains, the spectators dash towards either side of the stretch of sand, vying for good positions. The diversity of creatures gathered at Peril Sands is spectacular. All unite here, noisily cheering on the competitors, but silently they wish, most of all, that the peace wil! remain.

In the history of the Great Race, only one has made it to the finish line unhurt. Sanzoc, a Sand Creature from the Dodzin Desert, was born into a family of Racers. He trained his entire life for the Race and altered Namboodya's history when he won it. Arriving at the finishing line first, and with no injuries, earnt him the title of the Great Race Champion. His statue marks the finishing line.

Today, 14 Racers wait in grand tents filled with servants and gifts. Their family members parade into the tents to wish them luck and godspeed. The Racers not only have to travel the long distance to the finish line, they must also avoid treacherous obstacles. One of these are the Sand Suckers—little pockets in the sand that viciously suck at random. Any creature unfortunate enough to be standing on a Sand Sucker when it decides to suck, is lost to the sands forever.

The second hurdle the Racers face are the Flying Ferriers. These winged dog-like creatures inhabit the skies of Peril Sands. They swoop down and pick up large rocks in their mouths, dropping them to the ground when they become too heavy. The lucky competitors are only knocked unconscious by the falling boulders.

The 15th Racer in the competition sits alone in a plain tent of modest size, waiting for the sounds of the horns to announce the start of the race. Sashoc is a Sand Creature, from the Dodzin Desert, and the youngest of the competitors. She is also the great-granddaughter of Sanzoc.

Sashoc chews her nails nervously. Her whole village, indeed the entire race of Sand Creatures, is depending on her to win the race. The winner is given the privilege of stopping one of the many wars across the land of Namboodya. As her people will not survive another year of trying to prevent the vicious Desert Dopplers from taking their land, Sashoc must win!

The horns sound, alerting the thousands of spectators that the race is about to begin. Their cheers are deafening. Sashoc stands, clenching and unclenching her hands. She takes a deep breath and exhales slowly, sweeping aside the flap at the entrance to her tent.

THE GREAT RACE – 2

Use the text on page 19 to answer the questions.

❶ Literal

(a) Name:

   (i) *the place where the Great Race is held.*

   _____

   (ii) *the name of the Great Race Champion.*

   _____

   (iii) *the winged dog-like creatures who inhabit the skies.*

   _____

   (iv) *the enemy of the Sand Creatures.*

   _____

   (v) *the youngest competitor in the Great Race.*

   _____

   _____

   _____

❷ Deductive

(a) The Flying Ferriers drop rocks from the skies onto the competitors. Why are the competitors who are 'only knocked unconscious' lucky?

_____

_____

_____

(b) List some words and phrases to describe how you think Sashoc must be feeling before the Great Race.

(c) 'All unite here, noisily cheering on the competitors, but silently they wish, most of all, that the peace will remain.'

What do you think this sentence from the text means?

_____

_____

_____

❸ Evaluative

(a) Do you think that Sashoc, being the great-granddaughter of Sanzoc, had a choice about becoming a Racer? Explain your answer.

_____

_____

(b) Would you like to live in the land of Namboodya? Explain your answer.

_____

_____

THE GREAT RACE – 3

Use the text on page 19 to complete the activities.

You are Sashoc and it is a week before the Great Race. Complete your personal diary for the week, including details such as:

- everyday elements of your life such as where you live, what you eat and how you are affected by the war with the Desert Dopplers.

- your training regime so that you will be prepared for the Sand Suckers and Flying Ferriers.

- travelling to and arriving at Peril Sands.

5 days until the Great Race.

Today I ... _____

_____

_____

4 days to go!

_____

_____

_____

3 days until the race!

_____

_____

_____

2 days left!

_____

_____

_____

Tomorrow is the Great Race. Today, I must .....

_____

_____

_____

_____

Teacher information

Genre:

Mystery

Question types and comprehension strategies:

- Analyses and extracts information from a mystery narrative to answer literal, deductive and evaluative questions.
- Makes connections between himself/herself and a character from a fictional text.
- Summarises the events in a fictional text from a character's point of view.

Worksheet information:

The answers to Questions 2 and 3 on page 25 could be used by the pupils to conduct character role-plays with a partner.

Answers:

Page 24

1. (a) He was out of work.
   (b) (i) The sun shimmering on the dolphin's skin was very bright.
       (ii) dug/scrabbled; a leather sack full of gold coins
       (iii) grey, silky clothes; the tail of a dolphin
2. Teacher check
3. Teacher check

Page 25

Teacher check

Extension:

Read other mystery tales such as:

Antonio S and the mystery of Theodore Guzman by Odo Hirsch

Emily Eyefinger series by Duncan Ball

Encyclopedia Brown series by Donald J Sobol

The Roman mysteries series by Caroline Lawrence

THE DOLPHIN MYSTERY – 1

Read the mystery.

'This is the worst holiday I've ever been on', Hamish sighed, kicking at the sand.

Ingrid nodded. 'It was nice of Uncle Ray to let us stay at his beach house. But I can't stop thinking about Dad being out of work. There's not going to be much money around for a while.' She bit her lip and felt for her dolphin necklace. She had bought it at the fair that morning with her last bit of pocket money, from a gypsy woman with black, liquid eyes. It wasn't the sort of jewellery Ingrid normally liked, but somehow the woman had made her feel that she just had to own it.

'Look at that!'

Ingrid glanced up and saw Hamish pointing out to sea. There was a dolphin, swimming straight towards them. Ingrid scrambled to her feet and waded into the water. To her surprise, the dolphin glided up to her, its head bumping against her legs. Its skin was shimmering in the sun so brightly that Ingrid shut her eyes. Then she heard Hamish gasp and she opened them again. Her heart skipped a beat. The dolphin had vanished and in its place was a woman, with grey silky clothes and long tangled hair.

Ingrid shivered. 'Who … who are you?'

The woman uttered soft squeaks and clicks. Her gaze was fixed on something behind Ingrid.

'Do you w-want to go up there?' asked Ingrid. Her mouth was dry.

The woman nodded and looked down at the water. Ingrid could see that she didn't have legs or feet—she had the tail of a dolphin.

'We have to help her', said Ingrid. She prodded her brother, who seemed to be frozen to the spot. 'Come on, Hamish.'

Ingrid put her arm around the woman's waist and waited for Hamish to do the same. She steeled her muscles for a heavy weight, but the woman was surprisingly light. Ingrid and Hamish dragged her over the seaweed and up the deserted beach. Suddenly, she began to squeak excitedly, pointing at the sand.

'I don't understand', said Ingrid. She looked into the woman's black, liquid eyes.

'She wants us to dig', said Hamish. 'Don't you?'

The woman nodded. She wriggled and Hamish and Ingrid set her gently on the ground. Hamish crouched down and scrabbled in the sand but Ingrid stared at the woman. Who was she? What did she want? Ingrid knew she ought to feel scared, but instead she was filled with a sense of calm.

'There's something here!' Hamish said. He reached into the hole he'd made and pulled up a leather sack. Ingrid held her breath as her brother untied the silk cord. Her mouth fell open. The sack was full of gold coins.

'We're rich!' yelled Hamish.

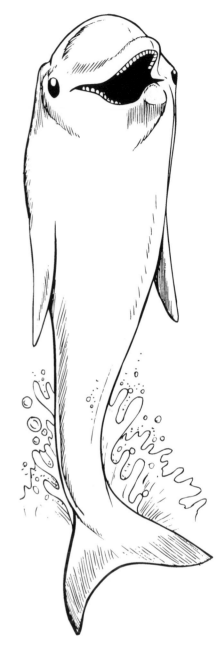

He scooped up some of the coins and threw them into the air, whooping for joy. Then he stared past Ingrid. 'She's gone', he said.

Ingrid whipped her head around and then jumped to her feet, scanning the sea. A dolphin was leaping in the air, far in the distance. Ingrid felt for her necklace and swallowed. What had happened? She had to go back to the fair to find out.

THE DOLPHIN MYSTERY – 2

Use the text to answer the questions.

❶ Literal

(a) What had happened to Ingrid and Hamish's dad?

_____

_____

(b) Complete these sentences.

(i) *Ingrid shut her eyes because* _____

_____

_____ .

(ii) *Hamish* _____

in the sand and found _____

_____ .

(iii) *The woman was wearing* _____

_____

and had _____
instead of legs and feet.

❷ Deductive

(a) List words to describe how Ingrid felt when:

(i) *she first saw the woman in the water.*

(ii) *she saw the dolphin leaping in the air.*

(b) Why do you think Hamish was 'frozen to the spot'?

_____

_____

_____

_____

❸ Evaluative

If you were Ingrid, what would you have done with the dolphin necklace until you got back to the fair?

☐ kept wearing it   ☐ thrown it away   ☐ put it in your pocket

☐ other _____

Write reasons for your answer.

_____

_____

_____

Primary comprehension   Prim-Ed Publishing   www.prim-ed.com

THE DOLPHIN MYSTERY – 3

Use the text on page 23 to help you complete this activity.

1 Imagine you are Ingrid. Complete a diary entry that summarises the events of the day described in the story. Use the facts that are given as well as your own ideas.

> Dear Diary
>
> This morning, I went to the fair ... _____
>
> _____
>
> _____
>
> _____
>
> This afternoon, Hamish and I went to the beach ... _____
>
> _____
>
> _____
>
> _____
>
> _____

2 Ingrid has decided to go back to the fair to talk to the gypsy woman. Write six questions you think she should ask to help her solve the mystery.

3 Circle one of the questions. Answer it as if you were the gypsy woman. You can be as mysterious as you like.

....

....

....

Teacher information

Genre:

Adventure

Question types and comprehension strategies:

- Analyses and extracts information from an adventure story to answer literal, deductive and evaluative questions.
- Makes a connection between the actions of a character in a text and himself/herself.

Worksheet information:

- Before commencing the activity on page 29, discuss the concept of time capsules with the class. Explain that some schools bury a time capsule containing examples of pupils' work and small mementos of the pupils' choice. These capsules might not be recovered for 10 or more years.
- Ask pupils to consider what they would choose to place in a 'tin box' like the one in the story. Pupils may like to volunteer some of their choices to prompt others.

Answers:

Page 28

1. (a) tin box, trees, ducks

   (b) Maddy's pigtails were lopsided.

   (c) small cars, toy soldiers, sports cards and old coins

2. Teacher check

3. Teacher check

Page 29

Teacher check

Extension:

- Pupils write the next chapter of the story, choosing one of the following events:
  - The children return to their boat to discover that the oars have drifted away across the lake.
  - While the boys are looking at the contents of the tin, Maddy wanders away and is bitten by a snake.
  - On the journey back, Sam falls out of the boat and begins to panic in the cold water.

Bowey Island – 1

Read the chapter from the adventure novel.

CHAPTER 4

The children collected the old boat from their grandfather's old shed, as they did at the beginning of every summer holidays. But this time they weren't rowing across the lake to Bowey Island to catch fish, or set up a tent or go swimming. This expedition had a purpose. They wanted to see if the map Ryan had found slipped inside a book in their grandparents' bookshelf was authentic.

'Put your life jacket on, Maddy', Ryan ordered. 'Sam, push us off!'

The children set off from the wooden jetty on their grandparent's property. Maddy sat in the bow, looking tiny in her bright yellow life jacket. Because she wasn't used to doing her own hair, her pigtails were lopsided, making her look like she might tip over at any minute.

After a silent trip (apart from the occasional grunt from Ryan struggling with the oars), the children arrived at the island.

'OK! The map says we have to find the tree with the largest trunk and stand facing the Bowey Estate', called Ryan.

Ryan walked quickly between the trees and bushes, dodging the sharp branches and prickly leaves. Maddy tried to follow her brother but a branch caught hold of one of her pigtails, causing her to yelp.

Sam caught up with his sister and, while he was untangling her from the tree's grasp, realised that this was the tree they needed. Ryan joined the pair and stood where he could see their grandparents' house through the bushes and trees.

'We need to walk ten paces and turn east. Hmmm … I wonder if that's east for real or east from the direction we are facing?' Ryan speculated. He decided to turn east from the house and step out the paces. Maddy and Sam followed him.

'OK! Now we must walk 13 paces and turn south and then another 11 paces. If we have followed the map correctly, then that is where we should dig.'

Maddy held up her miniature garden shovel that she had taken from the shed.

The children stepped out the number of paces and arrived at an area not far from the water's edge. Sam pointed out the duck prints in the mud.

Ryan and Sam began digging with their hands—scooping out the dirt into small piles. Maddy, crouched down by the site, clapped excitedly.

'I've found something!' Sam exclaimed. 'It feels like a tin.'

The boys retrieved an old tin box from the ground and opened it. Inside was a menagerie of little treasures—small cars, toy soldiers, some type of sports cards and old coins. It wasn't long before they realised that these were their father's things that he must have buried when he was a boy.

'Wait until we show these to Dad! I bet he has forgotten all about them!' said Sam, smiling.

BOWEY ISLAND – 2

Use the text on page 27 to answer the questions.

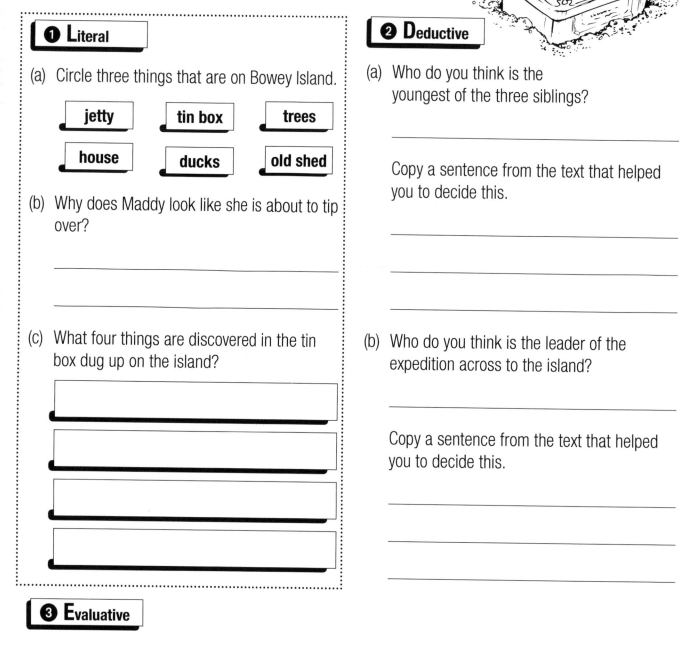

❶ Literal

(a) Circle three things that are on Bowey Island.

| jetty | tin box | trees |
| house | ducks | old shed |

(b) Why does Maddy look like she is about to tip over?

_____

_____

(c) What four things are discovered in the tin box dug up on the island?

[ ]

[ ]

[ ]

[ ]

❷ Deductive

(a) Who do you think is the youngest of the three siblings?

_____

Copy a sentence from the text that helped you to decide this.

_____

_____

(b) Who do you think is the leader of the expedition across to the island?

_____

Copy a sentence from the text that helped you to decide this.

_____

_____

❸ Evaluative

Complete each of the boxes about the adventure story *Bowey Island*.

Story genre	Title	Events and actions
Characters		
Setting		

Primary comprehension   Prim-Ed Publishing   www.prim-ed.com

Bowey Island – 3

Use the text on page 27 to complete the activities.

1 When the children's father was a boy, he collected his most prized possessions, placed them in a tin and buried them on Bowey Island. He was creating a 'time capsule' that showed what was important to him at the time.

Imagine you are going to create a time capsule and bury four of your most treasured items in it. What would they be and why would you choose them?

My first item would be because ...	**My second item would be** because ...
My third item would be because ...	**My fourth item would be** because ...

2 (a) Where would you bury your special tin?

....

(b) Why would you bury it there?

....

....

....

....

Prim-Ed Publishing   www.prim-ed.com   **Primary comprehension**

Genre:

Persuasive text

Question types and comprehension strategies:

- Analyses and extracts information from persuasive texts to answer literal, deductive and evaluative questions.
- Makes comparisons between two persuasive texts.
- Synthesises information about the conventions of persuasive texts to write a letter.

Worksheet information:

- Before commencing the activities on page 33, explain to the class that a 'rhetorical question' is a question that is designed to produce an effect, not receive an answer.
- Rhetorical questions are often used in persuasive texts to encourage readers to agree with the author's point of view. Review the questions used in the letters on page 31.
- After pupils have completed their letters, display them and read samples as a class. Decide which letter is the most persuasive and discuss why it is so effective.

Answers:

Page 32

1.

Letter 1	Letter 2
seating causes splinters	destroying native plants
seating has no back support	increasing effects of erosion
painful for parents to sit and watch children play sport	dunes won't be there for grandchildren to see
could cause permanent back injury	

2–3.   Teacher check

Page 33

Teacher check

Extension:

- Pupils study text that has been read in class and collect and investigate words which are used to persuade the reader; for example, rhetorical questions and keywords and phrases which encourage the reader to accept a point of view, such as, 'surely', 'moreover', 'because' etc.
- Pupils look in newspapers at the 'Letters to the editor' section and underline persuasive words and phrases.

BAKERSTOWN COUNCIL – 1

Read the persuasive texts.

BAKERSTOWN COUNCIL – Letter 1

Re: Seating at Bakerstown Sports Stadium

To whom it may concern

We would like to appeal to the Council for an urgent upgrade of the seating at the Bakerstown Sports Stadium.
Currently, the seating is a (not so) 'grand' stand of rough wooden planks that deliver cruel splinters to anyone who sits on them.

The planks have nothing to support a person's back and become excruciatingly uncomfortable after several hours of watching sport.

As we refuse to abandon our children during their moments of glory on the sporting fields, we urge the Council to consider the parents of this town who suffer the misfortune (and agony) of having to spend their Saturdays on the seating at the stadium.

It is essential that this matter be a priority for the Council before permanent back injury is caused to a spectator by the seating at the Bakerstown Sports Stadium. Surely it would be cheaper to upgrade the seating than pay medical expenses for injured spectators?

Karen O'Brien – Parents Committee of Bakerstown Primary School

BAKERSTOWN COUNCIL – Letter 2

Re: Baker's Beach sand dunes

To whom it may concern

I am writing to inform the Council of the tragedy that occurs every summer at Baker's Beach.

Beachgoers appear oblivious to the damage they are causing to the Baker's Beach sand dunes when they ignore the path from the car park to the ocean and, instead, trudge through the dunes.

I shudder to think that, with another summer approaching, kids will be sliding down the dunes on their 'boogie boards', crushing native plants and leaving the dunes bare and vulnerable. The effects of erosion will increase and the sand will be blown away and lost forever!

Do we want our grandchildren and their children to only be able to witness the beauty of the Baker's Beach sand dunes as photographs in books?

I implore the Council to construct a fence around the dunes and create warning signs to educate the people about their destructive behaviour before it is too late. We must protect our natural environment!

Jeff Baker – Bakerstown Coastal Care Organisation

BAKERSTOWN COUNCIL – 2

Use the texts on page 31 to answer the questions.

❶ Literal

Find three reasons in each letter that states why the Council should agree to what is being asked.

Letter 1	Letter 2

❷ Deductive

Choose three words from each letter that you think may help to persuade the Council; for example, 'surely'.

Letter 1

Letter 2

❸ Evaluative

(a) Tick who you think is more successful at persuading a reader to agree with his/her point of view.

Karen O'Brien ☐   Jeff Baker ☐

Explain your choice.

_____

_____

_____

(b) If the Bakerstown Council only has enough money to budget for one of the projects requested in the letters, which project do you think they should choose?

Stadium seating ☐   Sand dunes fencing ☐

Explain your choice.

_____

_____

_____

BAKERSTOWN COUNCIL – 3

Refer to the texts on page 31 to help you complete these activities.

You are a 'boogie boarder' who lives in Bakerstown. Your favourite activity in summer is sand boarding down the Baker's Beach sand dunes. You have seen flyers stating that the Council is considering putting up a fence around the dunes.

1 Think of three reasons why you want the Council to change its decision about the fence.

2 Write a persuasive letter to the Council that explains why you think it should change its decision about the fence at the Baker's Beach sand dunes.

BAKERSTOWN COUNCIL

RE: Sand dunes at Baker's Beach

To whom it may concern

Begin with a strong sentence that states your opinion.

Introduce your reasons and give examples.

Include persuasive words and phrases such as:
surely …
I think that …
You can see that …
Therefore …

Include a 'rhetorical question' to encourage the reader to agree with you.

Finish by repeating your opinion.

Genre:

Poetry

Question types and comprehension strategies:

- Analyses and extracts information from a poem to answer literal, deductive and evaluative questions.
- Makes comparisons between two poems.
- Scans a poem for relevant information.
- Makes connections between feelings expressed in a poem and his/her own feelings.

Worksheet information:

- Both of the poems are free verse, although *The troll* has a regular meter. The theme of both poems can be described as 'misunderstanding', 'prejudice' or 'being different'. Teachers may like to discuss these themes as well as poetic devices such as alliteration and repetition before the pupils complete the activity on page 37.

Answers:

Pages 35–36

1. (a) He would like to have a 'chinwag and chat'.
   (b) (i) sneering, teasing   (ii) den
       (iii) different   (iv) toes, noses
   (c) hurl, shove, spit out, stab
2. (a) Answers should indicate that they are harsh-sounding words.
   (b) Teacher check
   (c) Teacher check
3. Teacher check

Page 37

Teacher check

Extension:

- Encourage the pupils to find poems they like and perform them for the class with sound effects and movement.
- Collections of poems for children can be found in the following books:

  Walking on air by Berlie Doherty

  The new Oxford treasury of children's poems by Michael Harrison and Christopher Stuart-Clark

  I like this poem edited by Kaye Webb

THE TROLL/DIFFERENT – 1

Read the poems.

The troll

'Stay right away from the forest', they say
'The troll will catch you for sure.
He lurks near the lake,
He skulks in the shrubs
And he hides in the hollows of trees.'
'If he catches you, you'll be sorry', they say
'Boys and girls are his favourite lunch.
He thinks toes are tasty
Hair is like honey
And noses just so nice to nibble.'
They say anything to keep children away
From my den so deep in the woods
Where I eat luscious leaves,
Bright berries, sour seeds
And fresh fruit from the trificka tree.
I just can't believe they think I eat kids
Why would I want to do that?
I'd love to meet one
For a chinwag and chat –
A friend for a lonely old troll.
'Stay right away from the forest', they say.
'The troll's so ugly you'd faint.
He's nothing like us –
Just leave him alone
Some things don't deserve to be loved.'

Different

I am different from you
So
You hurl teasing words at me
Shove laughter in my face
Spit out lies about me
And stab hard stares in my eyes
All with a sneering smile
That shows your cruel heart
So
I am glad
I am different from you.

Use the poems to answer the questions.

1 Literal

(a) Why does the troll say he would like to meet a child?

_____

_____

(b) Complete these sentences.

(i) The person described in *Different* has a

_____ smile and

uses _____ words.

(ii) The troll lives in a

_____ in the woods.

(iii) The narrator of *Different* is glad to be

_____.

(iv) In *The troll*, 'they' believe the troll likes to eat children's hair,

_____ and

_____.

(c) List the four verbs used in *Different* that describe the actions of the person with the sneering smile.

_____

_____

_____

_____

THE TROLL/DIFFERENT – 2

Use the poems on page 35 to answer the questions.

❷ Deductive

(a) Why do you think the author of *Different* chose to use the words he/she did?

_____

_____

_____

(b) Who do you think 'they' are in *The troll*?

_____

_____

_____

_____

(c) List words you think describe the personality of the troll.

❸ Evaluative

(a) Do you agree that the troll 'doesn't deserve to be loved'? Explain why/why not.

_____

_____

_____

(b) What age do you imagine the narrator of *Different* to be?

☐ under 8   ☐ 8–12   ☐ teenager   ☐ adult

Give reasons for your answer.

....

....

....

....

Prim-Ed Publishing   www.prim-ed.com

THE TROLL/DIFFERENT – 3

Use the poems on page 35 to complete the activities.

1 Compare the two poems by completing the table.

	The troll	*Different*
Whose point of view is the poem from?		
Does the poem rhyme?	Yes No	Yes No
Is it divided into verses?	Yes No	Yes No
Does the poem tell a story or describe feelings?		
Is alliteration used (e.g. 'racing rabbits', 'dim and dusty room')? If yes, write an example.	Yes No	Yes No
Are any lines repeated? If yes, write an example.	Yes No	Yes No

2 (a) Look at the table. Circle the things the poems have in common.

(b) Name one other thing you noticed the poems have in common. _____

_____

3 Which poem did you prefer? ☐ *The troll* ☐ *Different*

Explain why. _____

_____

_____

4 How did your preferred poem make you feel? Describe another piece of writing or a situation that has also made you feel like this.

_____

_____

_____

Prim-Ed Publishing   www.prim-ed.com   **Primary comprehension**

THE GIANT WITH TEETH OF FIRE

Teacher information

Genre:

Folktale

Question types and comprehension strategies:

- Analyses and extracts information from a folktale to answer literal, deductive and evaluative questions.
- Uses sensory imaging to describe suitable visual and auditory effects for a film scene based on a text.

Worksheet information:

Before the pupils complete the activity on page 41, a class discussion could be held about effective visuals and sounds the pupils have experienced in their favourite films.

Answers:

Page 40

1. (a) The men had accidentally tickled his lips with one of the leaves.

   (b) 2, 1, 5, 4, 3

2. (a) Answers should indicate that the giant was pretending to be friendly.

   (b) Teacher check

3. Teacher check

Page 41

Teacher check

Extension:

- Information about the culture of the island of Rotuma can be found online at: http://www.hawaii.edu/oceanic/rotuma/os/hanua.html
- Collections of folktales from around the world can be found in the following books:

  Folktales and fables series by Robert Ingpen and Barbara Hayes

  Rich man, poor man, beggarman, thief: folk tales from around the world by Marcus Crouch

  The young Oxford book of folk tales by Kevin Crossley-Holland

THE GIANT WITH TEETH OF FIRE – 1

Read the folktale from the Pacific Islands.

Long ago, on the island of Rotuma, a giant lived in a cave high on a mountain. The villagers were terrified of him because his teeth blazed with fire. He only had to open his mouth or smile to make flames leap out and burn whatever was in front of him.

One day, some of the young men of the village decided they would try to steal the giant's fire. None of the villagers knew how to make fire, but they knew it would be useful. So the men gathered some dried coconut palm leaves and climbed up to the giant's cave. They breathed a sigh of relief when they found him sleeping. The men watched him for a while. Every time he exhaled, flames poured out and every time he inhaled, he sucked the flames back into his mouth.

When the men were ready, they crept towards the giant, holding their palm leaves up to his mouth. The next time the giant breathed out, the leaves caught alight. Excited, the men tiptoed out of the cave. They hadn't noticed that one of the leaves had tickled the giant's lips and woken him. He opened his eyes and stomped to the entrance of the cave. He saw the men racing down the mountain with their burning leaves.

'That's my fire!' the giant bellowed. He ran down the mountain after the men.

But the men were quick on their feet and reached their cave ahead of the giant. As soon as they got there, they heaved a boulder across the cave's entrance. Then they used their leaves to light a wood fire inside the cave.

A few moments later, the giant arrived. He roared and used all his strength to try to move the boulder, but it would not budge. Then he had an idea. He would trick the men into moving the boulder. Then he could stick his head into the cave and burn them up.

'I don't want to hurt you', the giant said in the softest voice he could manage. 'I want to be your friend. Move the boulder aside so I can sing to you.'

The men did not believe him, but they also did not want to stay in the cave forever, so they heaved the boulder a tiny distance, making a small gap the giant could see through.

'You won't be able to hear me sing through that gap', said the giant. 'Push the boulder further out of the way.'

By now, the young men had come up with a plan. 'Okay', they called. 'We'll move the boulder.'

The men shifted the boulder again until the giant could fit his head into the gap. But before he could open his mouth, the men pushed the boulder forward into his head, killing him instantly. His teeth were extinguished.

The men ran from the cave, shouting the news to the village. They shared the flames with all the villagers. From that time on, everyone on the island had a fire burning in their huts to cook their food and keep them warm at night.

THE GIANT WITH TEETH OF FIRE – 2

Use the text on page 39 to answer the questions.

❶ Literal

(a) What caused the giant to wake up?

_____

_____

(b) Order these events from 1 to 5.

☐ The giant chased the men down the mountain.

☐ The men gathered dried leaves.

☐ The giant's teeth were extinguished.

☐ The giant said he wanted to sing to the men.

☐ The men lit a wood fire.

❸ Evaluative

(a) Do you think the giant deserved to die?

☐ Yes   ☐ No   ☐ Maybe

Write reasons for your answer.

_____

_____

_____

_____

_____

_____

_____

❷ Deductive

(a) Why do you think the giant used a soft voice to talk to the men?

_____

_____

_____

_____

(b) Write points for and against this statement: 'The men in the folktale were clever'.

For

Against

THE GIANT WITH TEETH OF FIRE – 3

Use the text on page 39 to help you complete this activity.

Congratulations! You have been chosen to direct the film version of *The giant with teeth of fire*. The scriptwriters want you to make the film a thrilling experience for the audience. You begin by planning the most exciting scenes.

1 Describe two parts of the story you think will make exciting scenes.

- _____

  _____

  _____

- _____

  _____

  _____

2 Imagine each of the parts you have chosen as a film scene in your head. Write what you think the audience should see and hear. For example, 'The scene begins with a close-up of the giant's feet thundering on the ground. The camera moves to the villagers' horrified faces and we hear their screams over mournful music'.

Scene 1	Scene 2
Title: _____ _____	Title: _____ _____
Sights and sounds:	Sights and sounds:

Genre:

Horror

Question types and comprehension strategies:

- Analyses and extracts information from a horror narrative to answer literal, deductive and evaluative questions.
- Uses sensory imaging to create appropriate background information for a horror story text.
- Predicts likely events that could take place after the close of a horror story text.

Worksheet information:

Teachers may like to bring in some horror story texts to discuss with the class before the pupils complete the activities on page 45.

Answers:

Page 44

1. (a) 12

   (b) His mother had called him for dinner.

   (c) bed, in front of door, in front of Ryan's face

2. (a) Answers should include three of the following: starts to shiver or shudder; tries to scream for his parents; feels sweat prickling the back of his neck; staggers backwards and falls to his knees; whimpers to the clown

   (b)–(c) Teacher check

3. Teacher check

Page 45

Teacher check

Extension:

Horror authors for children include Neil Gaiman, Philip Pullman, Brian Selznick, Darren Shan and RL Stine.

Stop clowning around – 1

Read the horror narrative.

Ryan put the clown on his bookcase and pulled a face at it. He couldn't believe that his Aunty Jane would give him a present like that for his twelfth birthday. It was a soft toy meant for a little kid! She'd always given him such great presents up until now. And then this had arrived in the post yesterday. Without even a card.

'Ryan! Time for dinner!'

'Coming, Mum.' Ryan gave the clown one more disgusted glance and then raced down the stairs.

After dinner, he went up to his room to grab a book to read. His father was watching a boring programme on television and he didn't feel like playing on the computer.

As Ryan walked into the room, he suddenly started to shiver. Someone is watching me. The thought went through his mind before he could stop it. What had made him think that? He'd probably been watching too many scary films lately. But then he looked at his bookcase. The clown was missing. Ryan gasped and then laughed at himself when he saw it sitting on his bed. He must have put it there without realising. He shook his head and left the room. But it was strange. He was sure that it had been on the bookcase …

A few hours later it was bedtime. Ryan had almost forgotten about the clown until he walked into his room again. The same cold shudder went through him and his eyes went straight to his bed. The clown wasn't there.

Bang! Ryan's door slammed shut behind him. He whirled around. The clown was sitting in front of the door, its glassy eyes boring into Ryan's. Ryan tried to scream out for his parents, but the words got stuck in his throat. He reached out for the doorhandle, but some invisible force pushed him back. Ryan felt the sweat start to prickle the back of his neck. He looked down at the clown. Its face had contorted into a murderous expression. And then it started to rise, slowly and gently in the air, until it was directly in front of Ryan's terrified face.

Ryan tried to scream again, but his voice simply wouldn't work. He staggered backwards and fell to his knees.

'Please', he whimpered. 'Don't hurt me. What do you want? Why did Aunty Jane send you?'

STOP CLOWNING AROUND – 2

Use the text on page 43 to answer the questions.

❶ Literal

Use the text to answer the questions.

(a) How old is Ryan? _____

(b) Why did Ryan go downstairs?

_____

_____

(c) List the places the clown moves to.

Bookcase _____

_____

_____

_____

❸ Evaluative

(a) The author presents the clown as a
frightening object by making it come to life
and do unexpected things. Choose a toy
from the list below. Write a description of it
that makes it seem frightening.

☐ rag doll ☐ toy truck

☐ building blocks ☐ skipping rope

_____

_____

_____

_____

_____

❷ Deductive

(a) List three things Ryan does that
tell us he is uneasy or frightened.

```
┌─────────────────────────────┐
│                             │
│                             │
└─────────────────────────────┘
┌─────────────────────────────┐
│                             │
│                             │
└─────────────────────────────┘
┌─────────────────────────────┐
│                             │
│                             │
└─────────────────────────────┘
```

(b) The author does not tell us what the clown
looks like. Why do you think this might be?

_____

_____

_____

_____

(c) Describe and draw the clown as you
imagined it.

_____

_____

_____

_____

```
┌─────────────────────────────┐
│                             │
│                             │
│                             │
└─────────────────────────────┘
```

STOP CLOWNING AROUND – 3

Horror stories like the one on page 43 are designed to frighten a reader. They often contain supernatural events—such as ghosts, aliens or objects that come to life. The main character is usually in fear of his or her life.

Think carefully about the elements of a typical horror story to answer the following questions.

1 Invent a 'backstory' for the text on page 43. The 'backstory' is the important background information about the characters or events in the text.

Aunty Jane	The clown
Is Aunty Jane who Ryan thinks she is? Has something happened to her recently? Did she send the clown to Ryan or did someone else?	How has the clown come to life? Did someone or something help it do this? Why does the clown want to frighten Ryan? What is its goal?

2 Predict what might happen next to Ryan. Write two possibilities.

Primary comprehension

THE SALTCELLAR TRICK

Teacher information

Genre:

Procedure

Question types and comprehension strategies:

- Analyses and extracts information from a set of instructions to answer literal, deductive and evaluative questions.
- Determines the importance of information in a text to create a cartoon strip with dialogue.
- Uses sensory imaging to visualise himself/herself performing a magic trick.

Worksheet information:

After completing the activity on page 49, the pupils could be provided with suitable props to practise and perform the magic trick, with their 'patter', to younger pupils in the school.

Answers:

Pages 47–48

1. (a) On the table, under the serviette.

   (b) (i) True   (ii) True

        (iii) False   (iv) False

2. Teacher check

3. Teacher check

Page 49

Teacher check

Extension:

Books of magic tricks or practical jokes for children are easily found in a library. Some suitable titles include:

The practical jokers handbook by John Dineen

Magic tricks by Fay Presto

Amazing magic tricks by various authors

THE SALTCELLAR TRICK – 1

Read the magic trick instructions.

The trick:

You announce to your audience that you are going to use a saltcellar to push a coin through a table. You cover the saltcellar with a serviette and say some magic words … what happened? It's not the coin that has gone through the table—it's the saltcellar!

You will need:

• a saltcellar with a pointed top

• a coin

• a thick paper serviette

What to do:

1. Sit at a table and place the coin in front of you.

2. Put the saltcellar on top of the coin and cover it with the serviette. Give an excuse for why the serviette is needed. Place both of your hands firmly around the saltcellar to make sure the serviette takes on its shape.

3. Pick up the saltcellar, covered by the serviette, and move it over the edge of the table until it is above your lap.

4. Secretly drop the saltcellar into your lap. The serviette will keep its shape, making it look as if you are still holding the saltcellar.

5. Place the serviette back over the coin. Then quickly bang your fist on the serviette. Pretend to be amazed as the serviette flattens onto the table—the saltcellar has gone!

6. Reach under the table and secretly pick up the saltcellar from your lap. Then take a bow!

Use the text to answer the questions.

❶ Literal

(a) Where is the coin at the end of the trick? _____

(b) Tick true or false.

   (i) You need to sit at a table to perform this trick.

    True False

   (ii) When you begin the trick, the audience think that you want to make the coin go through the table.

   True False

   (iii) You could do this trick without covering the saltcellar.

    True False

   (iv) It is okay if the audience see you pick up the saltcellar from your lap.

   True False

THE SALTCELLAR TRICK – 2

Read the magic trick instructions.

❷ Deductive

(a) List some things that could go wrong with this trick. Why might it not work?

❸ Evaluative

What do you think makes a good magician? List some qualities you think the ideal magician should have.

(b) Why do you think:

(i) the serviette has to be thick?

_____

_____

_____

(ii) the audience are told that the coin, not the saltcellar, will disappear?

_____

_____

_____

(iii) the saltcellar must have a pointed top?

_____

_____

_____

(c) Do you think a child under the age of six could learn to do this trick? Explain why/why not.

_____

_____

_____

_____

_____

_____

The saltcellar trick – 3

Use the text on page 47 to help you complete this activity.

Magicians usually talk a lot while they are performing. They do this to help the audience understand what is happening (or what they want the audience to think is happening) and also to distract the audience from watching certain parts of the trick too carefully.

Imagine yourself performing the trick described on page 47. Create a cartoon strip showing the six steps. Write what you would say during each step of the trick. It should sound impressive to an audience.

1

_____
_____
_____
_____

2

_____
_____
_____
_____

3

_____
_____
_____
_____

4

_____
_____
_____
_____

5

_____
_____
_____
_____

6

_____
_____
_____
_____

Prim-Ed Publishing   www.prim-ed.com   **Primary comprehension**

Genre:

Play

Question types and comprehension strategies:

- Analyses and extracts information from a play to answer literal, deductive and evaluative questions.
- Determines the important elements of a play to write a plan.
- Writes a summary of a play.

Worksheet information:

Once the pupils have written their playscripts, they could rehearse them with a partner and then perform them for the class.

Answers:

Page 52

1. (a) She had broken a mirror and bought some shoes.
   (b) 4, 3, 2, 5, 1
   (c) The quiche Flynn was cooking for lunch.
2. (a) (ii) Natalie has just shown that she is superstitious too.
   (b) She cannot believe that Flynn is still superstitious.
3. Teacher check

Page 53

Teacher check

Extension:

Look for plays adapted from popular children's books; e.g.
Charlie and the chocolate factory by Roald Dahl
Charlotte's web by EB White
Hating Alison Ashley by Robin Klein
The lion, the witch and the wardrobe by CS Lewis

SUPERSTITIOUS – 1

Read the play.

Flynn is in his house, setting the table for lunch. He hears a knock on the front door and walks over to open it. His friend Natalie is standing there, carrying an umbrella and a shopping bag.

Natalie   Hi, Flynn! Thanks for inviting me for lunch. (*She points offstage.*) Is that your black cat? I almost tripped over it.

Flynn   No, that's the neighbour's cat. Don't tell me it crossed your path? That's very bad luck.

Natalie   (*sighing*) You're not still superstitious, are you?

Flynn   Well, maybe a bit. I just think it's best to avoid things that might be bad luck. Anyway, come in. It's great to see you.

Natalie   (*stepping inside*) Do you mind if I leave my umbrella here to dry? (*She opens it and props it against the wall.*)

Flynn   Natalie! Didn't I ever tell you it's bad luck to open an umbrella indoors?

Natalie   (*laughing*) I don't believe in things like that.

Flynn and Natalie walk into Flynn's kitchen.

Natalie   (*sniffing the air*) Mmm, what's that delicious smell?

Flynn   I've made a quiche. I know it's your favourite. Please sit down. It's nearly ready. (*Flynn gestures towards the kitchen table.*)

Natalie   Thanks. (*She sits down and puts her shopping bag on the table.*)

Flynn   (*sitting next to her*) What's in the bag?

Natalie   Just a pair of shoes I bought on the way here. They were on sale and …

Flynn   Oh, no. Take them off the table. Now!

Natalie   Why … oh, that's right. New shoes on the table are supposed to bring bad luck, aren't they? Okay, I'll take them off if it will make you feel better. (*She picks up the bag and puts it on the floor.*) I'd better not tell you about the mirror I broke this morning—that brings me bad luck too, doesn't it?

Flynn   (*groaning*) Yes—for the next seven years! (*He shakes his head.*) Let's change the subject. When do you go on your holiday?

Natalie   Tomorrow.

Flynn   But that's Friday the thirteenth! You can't go then!

Natalie   Flynn, I already told you I don't believe in all that nonsense about bad luck. And anyway (*reaching into her pocket*), I don't go anywhere without my four-leaf clover lucky charm. Touch wood – (*knocking on the table*) I'll be just fine.

Natalie looks puzzled as Flynn bursts out laughing.

SUPERSTITIOUS – 2

Use the text on page 51 to answer the questions.

❶ Literal

(a) Write two things Natalie had done before arriving at Flynn's house.

_____

_____

(b) Order these events (1–5) from the play.

☐ Natalie takes the shoes off the table.

☐ Flynn sits at the table.

☐ Flynn and Natalie walk into the kitchen.

☐ Natalie knocks on the table.

☐ Natalie opens her umbrella.

(c) What could Natalie smell?

_____

_____

❷ Deductive

Tick the best answer for this question.

(a) Why does Flynn laugh at the end of the play?

(i) He is looking forward to lunch. ☐

(ii) Natalie has just shown that she is superstitious too. ☐

(iii) He is having a good time. ☐

(iv) He thinks it will bring good luck. ☐

(b) Why do you think Natalie sighs near the beginning of the play?

[ ]

❸ Evaluative

Mark the scale to show how superstitious you are.

not at all   extremely

|_____|_____|_____|_____|

Explain your answer.

_____

_____

_____

_____

SUPERSTITIOUS – 3

The plans of stories and plays are constructed by authors in many different ways.
The author of the play on page 51 used the following steps:

- Decided on a suitable setting and characters for a short play about superstitions.
- Made a list of common bad and good luck superstitions.
- Thought of a series of events that would cause the characters to experience or discuss each bad luck superstition.
- Used the good luck superstitions to create a humorous ending.

1 Imagine you are the author of *Superstitious*. Write your plan for the play by following the steps above.

Setting

Characters

Relationship of characters
(e.g. 'friends', 'husband/wife' etc.)

Bad luck superstitions

- A black cat crossing your path
-
-

-
-

Good luck superstitions

-
-

Series of events

- Natalie tells Flynn she almost tripped over a black cat.
-
-
-

Ending

---

2 Use your answers to Question 1 to help you write a plan for your own play about superstitions. You can use some of the ideas from the original plan. Write your plan on a separate sheet of paper and then use it to write your playscript.

CINEMA SITUATION

Teacher information

Genre:

Letter to the editor

Question types and comprehension strategies:

- Analyses and extracts information from a letter to the editor to answer literal, deductive and evaluative questions.
- Scans a text for information to answer interview questions.
- Compares the decisions of a fictional character with those he/she might make about an issue.

Worksheet information:

After pupils have completed the activity on page 57, they could rehearse their interviews, with one pupil in each pair playing the journalist and the other playing an owner. The interviews could then be presented to the class.

Answers:

Page 56

1. (a) The snacks it sells are overpriced and it stocks a limited range of refreshments.

   (b) (i) False (ii) False (iii) True (iv) True

2. Teacher check

3. Teacher check

Page 57

Teacher check

Extension:

- Pupils could collect some interesting letters to the editor from local newspapers and discuss the issues contained in them.

CINEMA SITUATION – 1

Read the letter to the editor.

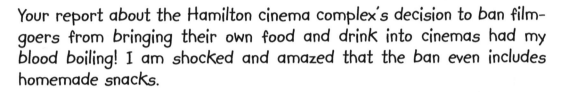

15 Wexford Place
HAMILTON

11 May 2005

The Editor
Western Ridge community newspaper
21 Knight Road
HAMILTON

Dear Madam

Your report about the Hamilton cinema complex's decision to ban film-goers from bringing their own food and drink into cinemas had my blood boiling! I am shocked and amazed that the ban even includes homemade snacks.

Not surprisingly, the cinema complex owners are perfectly happy for people to buy food at the cinema's snack shop. But the snacks offered for sale can be bought at any supermarket for less than half the price! The snack shop also stocks a limited range of refreshments. What if some film-goers are allergic to the products sold at the snack shop? Does this mean they have to go hungry or thirsty?

I am also wondering how the complex owners intend to police the ban. Should we expect bag checks by sniffer dogs before we are allowed in? Will 'illegal' snacks be confiscated?

The whole idea is simply ridiculous. All that it will achieve for the complex owners is to turn their customers away. Since hearing of the ban, I and many of my friends now prefer to drive an extra 10 minutes to go to the cinema in Newtown rather than give any money to these greedy people.

I am asking for all residents of Hamilton to boycott the cinema complex completely until its owners change this rule. We need to stand together on this issue. No-one should have the right to tell us what we can and can't eat!

Yours sincerely

Clare Warden

CINEMA SITUATION – 2

Use the text on page 55 to answer the question.

❶ Literal

(a) What does the writer dislike about the cinema snack shop?

_____

_____

_____

(b) Tick true or false.

   (i) The cinema complex owners are using sniffer dogs.

     True   False

   (ii) You could take a homemade cake into the Hamilton cinemas.

     True   False

   (iii) There is a cinema in Newtown.

     True   False

   (iv) The editor of the _Western Ridge_ community newspaper is a woman.

     True   False

❷ Deductive

(a) Why do you think the writer calls the Hamilton cinema complex owners 'greedy people'?

_____

_____

_____

(b) Do you think the Hamilton cinema complex owners have made a wise decision?

   Yes   No

Give reasons for your answer.

_____

_____

_____

_____

❸ Evaluative

Imagine you are trying to decide whether or not to join the writer's boycott of the cinema. Write a list of reasons for and against the boycott.

For	Against

CINEMA SITUATION – 3

Use the text on page 55 to help you complete this activity.

Find a partner to work with. Imagine you are the owners of the Hamilton cinema complex. A journalist from the *Western Ridge* community newspaper comes to see you to ask you some questions about your food and drink ban. He explains that the answers will be published in an article in the next issue of the newspaper.

Write your answers to the journalist's questions.

1 Why did you decide to ban people from bringing their own food and drink into your cinemas? Do you think this is fair?

_____

_____

_____

_____

2 Do you think you should improve your snack shop? Why/Why not?

3 People might try to smuggle 'banned' food and drink into your cinemas. How will you control this?

_____

_____

_____

4 What is your opinion of the letter to the editor written by Clare Warden, which was published recently in our newspaper?

5 Will you change your minds about your decision? Why/Why not?

_____

_____

_____

_____

_____

_____

LEONARDO DA VINCI

Teacher information

Genre:

Biography

Question types and comprehension strategies:

- Analyses and extracts information from a biography to answer literal, deductive and evaluative questions.
- Scans a biography for facts to complete a time line.
- Scans a biography for facts about a person's achievements.
- Makes connections between an individual from a biography and himself/herself.

Worksheet information:

The answers given by the pupils on page 61 could be used as a springboard for creative writing activities; e.g. playscripts, descriptions etc.

Answers:

Page 60

1. (a) He travelled and worked around Italy.
   (b) *The baptism of Christ*, *The last supper* and the *Mona Lisa*.
2. (a) (i)   Opinion   (ii)   Opinion
         (iii) Fact   (iv)   Opinion
   (b) Teacher check
   (c) Teacher check
3. Teacher check

Page 61

Teacher check

Extension:

- Further information about Leonardo da Vinci can be found by entering his name into a search engine. Some useful websites include:
  http://www.mos.org/sln/Leonardo/
  http://www.lairweb.org.nz/leonardo/
- Pupils can use an Internet search engine to find out about the life of a person that interests them and use it to write a profile about him/her.

Leonardo da Vinci – 1

Read the biography.

Leonardo da Vinci is regarded as one of the greatest geniuses of all time. He was a skilled artist, inventor, architect and scientist—among other things!

Da Vinci was born in 1452 near the town of Vinci in Italy. As a teenager, he became an apprentice to a well-known artist, Andrea del Verrocchio, in the city of Florence. During this time, da Vinci learnt painting, sculpting and other crafts. When he was about 21, Verrocchio let him paint part of an important painting, *The baptism of Christ*.

In 1483, da Vinci became the court artist and engineer for the Duke of Milan. During his 16 years in Milan, da Vinci designed forts, weapons, sets for plays and canal systems. He also wrote his ideas on a vast range of subjects, from human anatomy to flying machines. Amazingly, he even found time to work on many paintings, although he left dozens of these unfinished. One that he did manage to complete was the famous wall mural, *The last supper*.

In 1499, da Vinci had to flee Milan when it was attacked by French troops. He then spent several years travelling and working around Italy. In 1516, he was invited to France to become the official painter, engineer and architect for King Francis I. Here he completed plans for buildings, sketches of animals and machines and studies on the nature of water.

Da Vinci died in France in 1519. He had recorded his ideas, observations, plans and sketches in a series of notebooks throughout his life but, unfortunately, these were not found until hundreds of years after his death. In the meantime, other people came up with the same or similar ideas. You may be surprised to learn that some modern inventions were once drawn or described by da Vinci.

Just a few examples of da Vinci's achievements include the following.

- He drew plans for a type of helicopter, an aeroplane, military weapons, parachutes and submarines.
- He was the first scientist to study the flight of birds.
- He drew the first correct representations of human body parts like bones, muscles and organs. He got his information from studying human corpses.
- He painted the *Mona Lisa*, one of the most famous paintings in the world.
- He was very interested in water and imagined inventions like underwater breathing devices, life preservers, shoes to help you walk on water and swimming fins.

Think about Leonardo da Vinci the next time you ride a bike. He even came up with a design for that— hundreds of years before it was actually invented!

Leonardo da Vinci – 2

Use the text to answer the questions.

❶ Literal

(a) What did da Vinci do between 1499 and 1516?

_____

(b) List the titles of three paintings da Vinci worked on.

❷ Deductive

(a) Tick 'fact' or 'opinion' for each statement.

(i) Da Vinci should have published his ideas in books.   **FACT** | **OPINION**

(ii) Da Vinci is the smartest person ever to have lived.   **FACT** | **OPINION**

(iii) Most of da Vinci's life was spent in Italy.   **FACT** | **OPINION**

(iv) Da Vinci should have concentrated on one occupation.   **FACT** | **OPINION**

(b) Why do you think da Vinci is regarded as a genius?

_____

_____

(c) What do you think was da Vinci's greatest achievement?

_____

Explain why.

_____

_____

_____

❸ Evaluative

One of da Vinci's ideas for an invention was shoes that could help you walk on water. Why might these be useful for a person or a company to own? List some ideas below.

Leonardo da Vinci – 3

Use the text on page 59 to help you complete this activity.

Imagine that Leonardo da Vinci invents a time machine in 1516. He uses it to travel forward in time to the present day. You are lucky enough to be chosen to interview him.

1 Prepare your interview by noting some background information on da Vinci. Complete a time line of important events in his life and list some of his great achievements.

Time line
1452
1473
1483
1499
1516

Examples of achievements

Art _____

_____

_____

Science _____

_____

_____

Inventive ideas _____

_____

_____

2 Based on your answers, write three questions you would like to ask da Vinci.

- _____
- _____
- _____

3 Da Vinci tells you he is interested in seeing some modern inventions. List three things you would like to show him. Explain why you think he would be interested in each one.

THE PAINTING IN THE SHED

Teacher information

Genre:

Report

Question types and comprehension strategies:

- Analyses and extracts information from a newspaper report to answer literal, deductive and evaluative questions.
- Scans a text for different points of view.
- Predicts the likely reactions of a fictional person.

Worksheet information:

After completing the activity on page 65, the pupils could create their own newspaper reports of incidents that involve different points of view.

Answers:

Page 64

1. (a) (i) 2   (ii) 19th
       (iii) 24   (iv) 14

   (b) art museums in France

   (c) (i) art historian   (ii) artist
       (iii) schoolteacher   (iv) artist and historian

2. Teacher check

3. Teacher check

Page 65

Teacher check

Extension:

- Collect reports from newspapers and the Internet. Discuss the type of language used by the majority of the reports.

THE PAINTING IN THE SHED — 1

Read the newspaper report.

GARDEN SHED FIND 'WORTH MILLIONS', SAYS EXPERT

A young schoolteacher has found a painting in her garden shed that has caused great excitement among art historians—and could be worth millions.

Genevieve Sinclair, 24, was cleaning out the shed when she discovered an oil painting of a cat sitting in front of a fireplace.

'The painting was given to me by my grandfather just before he died, two years ago', said Miss Sinclair. 'He bought it at a flea market in France. I had completely forgotten it was in the shed. Although Grandad always told me it was valuable, I didn't really believe him. I had always disliked the painting and thought I would try to sell it in a car boot sale.'

That was until an artist friend of Miss Sinclair's saw the painting and spotted the signature scrawled in the bottom corner—'Claude Morel'. He urged Miss Sinclair to take the painting to a local university. And it was there, in the company of art historian Eric Clifton, that Miss Sinclair discovered the painting's true worth.

'Most people will know Claude Morel's name—he was an important French artist of the nineteenth century', said Mr Clifton. 'It was thought that all of his works were held in various art museums in France. But this painting was unknown. It is definitely his. The signature matches perfectly and he has written his age—14—underneath the painting, as he did with all of his works. He also did many paintings of cats. This find could be worth millions for Miss Sinclair.'

Other art experts, however, don't share Mr Clifton's enthusiasm. Many are suggesting that the painting is a fake.

'I have examined the painting and I don't believe it was painted by Morel', says renowned French artist and historian, Guy Marceau. 'The style is completely different from all of his other paintings. Also, Claude Morel's diaries tell us that he did not begin painting until he was at least 15. I have written three books on the life of Morel and I can assure you they are 100 per cent correct in every detail. None of my research shows that he completed this painting.'

It appears that Miss Sinclair will have to wait at least six months before experts can tell her whether or not the painting is genuine. In the meantime, she admits she is dreaming about all the money she might make.

'It would completely change my life', she said. 'I can't wait to find out whether or not I am a millionaire.'

– Michael Tilly, London

THE PAINTING IN THE SHED – 2

Use the text on page 63 to answer the questions.

❶ Literal

(a) Number quiz!

(i) *How many years ago did Miss Sinclair's grandfather die?*

(ii) *In which century did Morel complete his paintings?*

(iii) *How old is Miss Sinclair?*

(iv) *What is written under Morel's signature on the painting found in Miss Sinclair's shed?*

(b) Where could you go to see a collection of Morel's paintings?

_____

(c) List the occupations of each of these people.

(i) **Eric Clifton**

_____

(ii) **Claude Morel**

_____

(iii) **Genevieve Sinclair**

_____

(iv) **Guy Marceau**

_____

❷ Deductive

(a) Write an alternative, eye-catching headline for this article.

(b) List three emotions Miss Sinclair might have felt when she first saw the painting in her shed.

❸ Evaluative

Imagine you are Miss Sinclair and you have been told the painting is genuine. You will soon be a millionaire! What will you do with the money?

_____

_____

THE PAINTING IN THE SHED – 3

Use the text on page 63 to complete the activity.

1 Do you think the painting will turn out to be genuine or a fake?
Write a summary of the evidence given by Miss Sinclair and the two
experts to help you make up your mind. Then write your opinion.

Evidence

Miss Sinclair _____

_____

_____

Mr Clifton _____

_____

_____

Mr Marceau _____

_____

_____

Based on the evidence, I think the painting is ☐ genuine ☐ a fake

because ... _____

_____

2 Write what you think each person mentioned in the article would say or do in reaction to each
announcement in the newspapers.

'Morel painting is genuine'	*'Morel painting is a fake'*
Miss Sinclair	*Miss Sinclair*
Mr Clifton	*Mr Clifton*
Mr Marceau	*Mr Marceau*

BLAZE DESTROYS SCHOOL

Teacher information

Genre:

Newspaper article

Question types and comprehension strategies:

- Analyses and extracts information from a newspaper article to answer literal, deductive and evaluative questions.
- Synthesises information from a text to piece together clues.
- Writes a summarising paragraph.

Worksheet information:

- Pupils reread the text and highlight the pieces of evidence in the text. These may include:
  - Valerie Draper hearing an explosion first then seeing smoke.
  - Jim Blackwood leaving work early (so perhaps not very dedicated to his job).
- Megan Warner noticing mice in storeroom.
- Jim Blackwood refusing to answer calls from the journalist.
- Two other schools have had fires that have begun in the science laboratory.

Answers:

Page 68

1. (a)   5, 6, 2, 3, 1, 4
    (b)   (i) False   (ii) True   (iii) False
          (iv) False   (v) False
2. Teacher check
3. Teacher check

Page 69

Teacher check

Extension:

- Organise for newspapers to be available to the class. Pupils read articles and choose one that appeals to them. The pupils highlight the keywords and phrases of the article and write a summarising paragraph that records the main idea of the article.
- Pupils look at a number of different newspaper articles and writes a list of the components of a newspaper article.

Read the newspaper report.

WOODVALE MORNING HERALD

17 August

BLAZE DESTROYS SCHOOL!

Fourth school in area in past 11 years to be destroyed by fire during summer holidays.

Sirens were heard at Woodvale Secondary School yesterday afternoon, but it wasn't the school siren declaring the end of a school day—it was the shrill sound of fire sirens.

The school, which has been closed for the last four weeks for the summer holidays, was a mass of flames, smoke and ash yesterday afternoon. The Woodvale Fire Department was contacted at 2.30 pm after a local resident, Mrs Valerie Draper, heard a loud bang ... 'almost like a firework exploding' and noticed smoke coming from the school.

The fire crew arrived to find the science laboratory and neighbouring classrooms blazing. The team were successful in preventing the fire from spreading to the rest of the school.

The headteacher of Woodvale Secondary School, Pat Staines, arrived moments after the fire was extinguished. Mrs Staines was concerned about the whereabouts of caretaker, Jim Blackwood, as he was hired to be at the school until 4.00 pm each day of the holidays.

Mr Blackwood was contacted and found to be at home. He told police that, due to the extremely hot weather, he had left the school at 2.00 pm that day.

Mrs Staines commented that, before the holidays, the science teacher, Miss Megan Warner, had noticed mouse droppings in the chemical storeroom—a small room attached to the science laboratory. She had informed the headteacher of her findings, concerned that mice running around in the storeroom could knock chemicals from their shelves. Those chemicals could possibly mix together on the floor of the storeroom—with the potential to cause an explosion and, ultimately, a fire.

Mrs Staines had asked Mr Blackwood to take care of the mice situation in the chemical storeroom over the holidays. We have been unsuccessful in our attempts to get Mr Blackwood to confirm whether he had removed the mice from the storeroom or not.

Woodvale Secondary School is the fourth school in the local area in the past 11 years to have been damaged by fire during the six-week summer break. Although one school had been the victim of an arsonist, the other two fires had begun in the science laboratories.

BLAZE DESTROYS SCHOOL – 2

Use the text on page 67 to answer the questions.

❶ Literal

(a) Put the chain of events in order from 1– 6, with 1 happening first and 6 last.

☐ The headteacher, Pat Staines, arrives at the school.

☐ Journalist asks Jim Blackwood about mice.

☐ Valerie Draper calls emergency services to report a fire.

☐ Fire-engine sirens are heard in the town of Woodvale.

☐ Jim Blackwood leaves the school and goes home.

☐ Firefighters extinguish the fire.

(b) Decide if these statements are true or false.

(i) Pat Staines called the fire department to report the fire.

True **False**

(ii) Megan Warner is the science teacher at Woodvale Secondary School.

True **False**

(iii) Jim Blackwood left the school early because of the fire.

True **False**

(iv) In the past, two schools in the area have been damaged by arsonists.

True **False**

(v) The pupils at Woodvale will be returning to school in one week.

True **False**

❷ Deductive

(a) List some words and phrases to describe how you think the headteacher felt when she saw the fire-engines in front of her school.

(b) Do you think the noise that Mrs Draper heard could help explain the cause of the fire? Explain your answer.

_____

_____

_____

(c) Do you think Jim Blackwood is avoiding answering the journalist? Why do you think this is?

_____

_____

_____

❸ Evaluative

(a) List three things the headteacher of Woodvale Secondary School will need to organise now.

BLAZE DESTROYS SCHOOL – 3

Use the text on page 67 to complete the activity.

You are a police officer at the Woodvale Police Department and have been assigned the task of writing the report about the fire at the school. There are three parts to the report.

- You must interview and collect a comment from each person involved.
- You must report on four pieces of evidence that may help to show the cause of the fire.
- You must write a final summarising paragraph regarding the cause of the fire.

POLICE REPORT

Scene: _____

Officer's name: _____

Date: _____

Person involved	Comment about cause of fire
Headteacher Pat Staines	
Science teacher Megan Warner	
Caretaker Jim Blackwood	
Fire chief Rick Renton	

Evidence

Evidence 1:

Evidence 2:

Evidence 3:

Evidence 4:

Final comments:

_____

_____

THE FIRST SPIDER

Teacher information

Genre:

Myth

Question types and comprehension strategies:

- Analyses and extracts information from a myth to answer literal, deductive and evaluative questions.
- Uses synthesis to consider different points of view on the events in a text.
- Summarises the events of a text from a character's point of view.
- Makes connections between the events of a text and his/her own opinions.

Worksheet information:

After the pupils complete the activity on page 73, the answers could be used as the basis for a debate, creative writing activities or a play.

Answers:

Page 72

1. (a) (i) True   (ii) False   (iii) False
   (iv) True
   (b) Both tapestries showed the gods.
2. Teacher check
3. Teacher check

Page 73

Teacher check

Extension:

- More Greek myths can be found in the following books:
  Favourite Greek myths by Lilian Stoughton Hyde
  Greek myths and legends by Anthony Masters
  The Orchard book of Greek myths by Geraldine McCaughrean
- Read myths from different cultures and compare the common themes. There are many books available which contain collections of myths from around the world.

The First Spider – 1

Read the Ancient Greek myth.

There once was a woman named Arachne who wove beautiful tapestries on her loom. She was so skilled that people came from far away to watch her using her weaving shuttle and thread. They paid great sums of money for her work.

Arachne was very proud of her weaving and boasted about her skills to anyone who would listen.

'I am the best weaver in the world', she said one day. 'I am far better than any god or goddess.'

An old woman standing nearby heard what she said. 'Do you think you are even better than the goddess Athene?' she asked.

Arachne nodded. 'Of course', she said, her nose in the air.

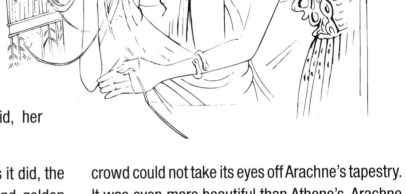

Just then, a strong wind whipped up. As it did, the old woman's grey hair became long and golden and her threadbare coat transformed into a white robe and silver breastplate. Then the woman grew taller and taller. Arachne blinked. There, towering over her, stood the goddess Athene.

'So you think you weave better tapestries than I do?' asked Athene. 'Let us find out. You and I will compete to see who is the best weaver in the world.'

Arachne felt a little frightened, but she did not think she could be beaten. She agreed and the contest began. A crowd gathered to watch.

Athene wove a tapestry that showed the gods performing heroic deeds. They appeared kind, clever and handsome. The crowd were stunned by the tapestry's beauty.

Arachne wove a tapestry that showed the gods in a less favourable light. They were playing tricks, lazing about, showing off and arguing. But the crowd could not take its eyes off Arachne's tapestry. It was even more beautiful than Athene's. Arachne had made the scene in her tapestry come to life.

Athene looked carefully at her tapestry and then at Arachne's. 'You win', she said. 'Your tapestry is better than mine.'

Arachne smiled. 'I told you so', she said.

The goddess frowned. 'But you are too proud, Arachne. And you have made fun of the gods. You must be punished. Never again will people appreciate your work.'

With that, the goddess pushed Arachne's shuttle into her mouth. Instantly, Arachne's body began to transform. Her arms became stuck to her sides, leaving her long fingers waving about. Her body became tiny, round and black. Arachne had become the first spider.

To this day, spiders weave beautiful webs but they are rarely admired. Most people prefer to knock them down or sweep them away.

THE FIRST SPIDER – 2

Use the text on page 71 to answer the questions.

❶ Literal

(a) Tick true or false.

    (i) Arachne was a boastful person.

    ☐ True ☐ False

    (iii) Arachne's tapestries were cheap to buy.

    ☐ True ☐ False

    (ii) Athene wore a golden breastplate.

    ☐ True ☐ False

    (iv) Arachne's arms became stuck to her sides.

    ☐ True ☐ False

(b) What did Athene's and Arachne's tapestries have in common? _____

_____

❷ Deductive

(a) Why do you think Athene:

    (i) *disguised herself as an old woman?* _____

_____

    (ii) *frowned at Arachne?* _____

_____

    (iii) *turned Arachne into a spider?* _____

_____

❸ Evaluative

(a) If you were Arachne, would you have agreed to the weaving contest? Explain why/why not.

_____

_____

_____

_____

(b) Write a new ending for the myth after the line 'Never again will people appreciate your work'. For example, you might have Athene turn Arachne into a different animal.

_____

_____

_____

_____

THE FIRST SPIDER – 3

Use the text on page 71 to help you complete this activity.

1 Imagine that Zeus, the king of the Greek gods, calls Athene and Arachne before him and asks for an explanation for what happened. Summarise the events in the story from each character's point of view. Include Athene's opinion of Arachne and Arachne's opinion of Athene.

Athene	Arachne

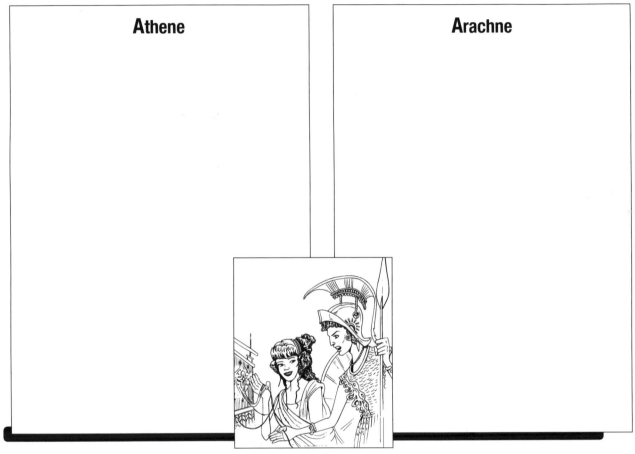

2 After listening to the evidence, Zeus gives a written judgment on what happened to Arachne. Write what you think it might say.

....

....

....

....

....

....

....

3 What do you think about what happened? Do you think it is fair that Arachne was punished for showing off? Give reasons for your answer.

....

....

....

....

....

....

....

....

FIRSTBORN FURY!

Teacher information

Genre:

Discussion

Question types and comprehension strategies:

- Analyses and extracts information from a discussion text to answer literal, deductive and evaluative questions.
- Scans a text for information.
- Paraphrases information from a text to complete a discussion template.

Worksheet information:

Prior to the activity, conduct a brief survey to determine how many children in the class are the oldest, the middle, the youngest etc.

Answers:

Pages 75–76

1. (a) (i)   Fact   (ii) Opinion
       (iii) Opinion   (iv) Fact
       (v) Opinion   (vi) Opinion

   (b) The writer suggests wrapping oneself in an invisibility cloak once a new baby arrives in the family.

   (c) The toddler is referred to as a 'tiny tornado' because he/she slobbers over toys and bulldozes constructions to the ground.

2. Teacher check

3. Teacher check

Page 77

   Teacher check

Extension:

- Pupils use the template on page 77 to write a discussion from a different point of view. Pupils rewrite their text in polished form and ask a partner to read it, checking that it makes sense and that the criteria for a discussion have been met.
- Extend the activity further, by preparing pupils for a 'mini-debate' that focuses on the pros and cons of being the oldest/youngest etc.

FIRSTBORN FURY! – 1

Read the text.

Being the oldest child in the family is just one big headache!

As the firstborn, you have your mum and dad all to yourself and everything is perfect! Every little thing you do is new and cute, and hundreds of pictures are taken, capturing your every expression and new trick.

This all changes the minute a new baby arrives. You might as well wrap yourself in an invisibility cloak because the only time you are called is when you are needed to 'help with the baby' or when you are getting scolded for 'attention-seeking behaviour'!

As the baby grows, your toys are slobbered over and clever constructions bulldozed to the ground by the tiny tornado known as the 'toddler'. Parents, who had always been fair and listened to your cries of injustice in the past, now respond to your complaints with sickening comments like 'But he's just a baby!'

Once the younger sibling is old enough to go to school, your whole world changes again. The walk to school, which had once been a great time to catch up with your friends, is now shadowed by a dark cloud known as responsibility! Do you have any idea how stressful it is trying to make a menacing munchkin hold your hand and look 'left, right, left' before crossing the street?

Once he/she is at your school, you are never free! You could be playing basketball with your friends at lunchtime—about to make a wicked three-pointer—when 'younger sibling' runs up to you complaining about a nasty 'bigger kid'. (Do I look like a bodyguard?) Your friends look at you like it is your 'duty' to go and defend the little terror.

In general, the oldest sibling is given a raw deal! We are disappointed once we realise we are not the centre of our parents' universe, our toys and games suffer, and we are burdened with the extra responsibilities that come with being the 'oldest'. Please, Mums and Dads, show some sympathy for your firstborn—especially when shopping for our next birthday present!

---

1 Literal

(a) Fact or opinion?

  (i) The writer has a younger sibling.

    | FACT | OPINION |

  (ii) The younger sibling is a boy.

    | FACT | OPINION |

  (iii) The writer has a birthday coming up.

    | FACT | OPINION |

  (iv) The writer likes to play basketball.

    | FACT | OPINION |

  (v) All little brothers and sisters break toys.

    | FACT | OPINION |

  (vi) It is easier being the youngest child than it is being the oldest.

    | FACT | OPINION |

FIRSTBORN FURY! – 2

Use the text on page 75 to answer the questions.

(b) What event causes the writer to suggest using an invisibility cloak?

_____

_____

_____

(c) Why does the writer refer to a toddler as a 'tiny tornado'?

_____

_____

_____

❷ Deductive

(a) What do you think the writer means by 'attention-seeking behaviour'? Give an example.

_____

_____

_____

_____

(b) Write words and phrases to describe how you think the writer feels when his toys are 'slobbered over' and broken by a younger brother or sister.

❸ Evaluative

(a) *'Your friends look at you like it is your 'duty' to go and defend the little terror.'*

Do you think it is an older sibling's 'duty' to protect younger brothers and sisters from children who bully them in school? | Yes | No |

Explain your answer.

_____

_____

_____

(b) Do you think there might be times when the older sibling likes having a younger brother or sister? | Yes | No |

Give reasons and examples.

_____

_____

_____

Firstborn fury! – 3

Use the text on page 75 to help you complete this activity.

A discussion is written to persuade others to a particular point of view. Discussions follow a set structure.

Find examples in the text for each of the following. Do not copy the sentences exactly—write the main idea.

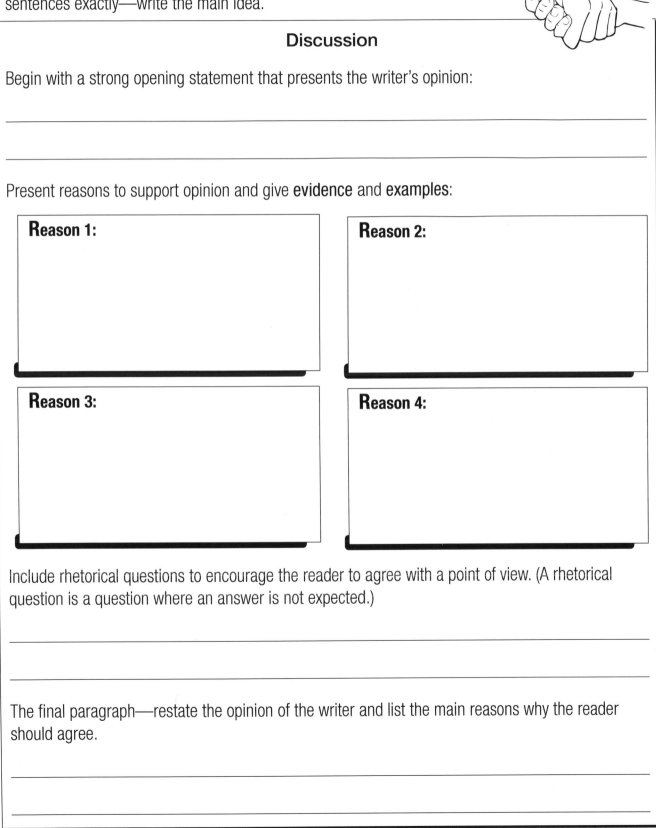

Discussion

Begin with a strong opening statement that presents the writer's opinion:

_____

_____

Present reasons to support opinion and give **evidence** and **examples**:

Reason 1:

Reason 2:

Reason 3:

Reason 4:

Include rhetorical questions to encourage the reader to agree with a point of view. (A rhetorical question is a question where an answer is not expected.)

_____

_____

The final paragraph—restate the opinion of the writer and list the main reasons why the reader should agree.

_____

_____

Genre:

Science fiction

Question types and comprehension strategies:

- Analyses and extracts information from a science fiction text to answer literal, deductive and evaluative questions.
- Paraphrases the main ideas and moral of a story.
- Determines the importance of information in a text to create a storyboard strip.

Worksheet information:

Before completing the activity on *Change your life – 3*, the class could discuss their answer to Question 3(b) on *Change your life – 2*. Do the pupils believe that Bailey will keep his promise by being more active and spending less time playing computer games?

Answers:

Page 80

1. (a) 3, 1, 2, 5, 4

   (b) Bailey jumped and ran in midair to avoid being struck by sharp star-shaped objects that were being thrown at him by a monkey.

2. (a) No: Bailey had a routine that helped him to get through the 'long' school day.

   (b) Teacher check

   (c) Teacher check

3. Teacher check.

Page 81

Teacher check

Extension:

- Collate data from the class about how the pupils spend their free time. Create a class graph of the information. Compare the results of time spent playing computer games (or in front of a television screen) to time spent being active. Hold discussions with the class regarding the results. In groups, pupils create an action plan to increase the time all children spend being active.
- Read other science fiction stories, such as:

  Northern lights by Philip Pullman

  The angel factory by Terence Blacker

  The exchange student by Kate Gilmore

  Earthborn by Sylvia Waugh

  Space race by Sylvia Waugh

CHANGE YOUR LIFE! – 1

Read the science fiction story.

Bailey had a routine that helped him to get through the 'long' school day. He would trot home, drop his bag by the door and sit in front of the television playing his X-box™ from 3.30 pm until he was called to dinner. Each day, Bailey sat, entranced, trying to master his latest game.

This particular day, although graphics were flashing across the television screen and bleeps and explosions could be heard coming from it, Bailey was nowhere to be seen. If anyone had walked past and looked closely at the screen, they would have seen Bailey shielding himself behind a tall, white pillar. Enormous glowing orange boulders, straight from the pit of a volcano, were rolling heavily towards him. The pillar next to Bailey's was struck by a fiery boulder, shattering it into hundreds of pieces and causing a loud explosion.

'This has to be a dream!' Bailey thought to himself. 'It just has to be!'

Bailey looked around at the strange world he found himself in. The sky was coal-black and absent of stars. The ground was a brilliant, emerald green, completely flat and so hard it felt like glass. Although he struggled to believe it, Bailey recognised the scenery as one constructed using the latest computer graphics.

Bailey squeezed his eyes tightly shut and thought, 'How can I be inside a game?'

He slowly opened his eyes, wishing that the lounge room he spent every afternoon sitting in would appear, but instead, a strange looking monkey wearing red overalls was staring angrily at him.

'Woosh!'

A very shiny and extremely sharp looking star-shaped object spun dangerously close to Bailey's left ear. The monkey reached into its backpack to retrieve another. Bailey, not waiting around for the monkey's aim to improve, turned and ran. Another star skimmed by his right knee. Bailey jumped up and somehow managed to keep running in midair. He spotted a boulder that had changed from sizzling orange to an earthy brown. It looked safe enough, so he hid behind it.

'This … is … not …' Bailey started to say, but he couldn't catch his breath to speak. He was wheezing heavily, his chest heaving, and sweat ran into his eyes.

'If I ever get out of here,' Bailey thought to himself, 'I promise to play more sport and less X-box™!'

Instantly, Bailey felt a strange pulling sensation in his stomach. It was as if something was trying to turn him inside out.

In a flash, Bailey found himself sitting cross-legged on the carpet in front of the television. As if it were a snake about to bite him, Bailey dropped the game controller from his hands then leant forward and turned the television off.

He spotted the cover of the game he had been playing and remembered that a man had handed it to him outside the entrance to his favourite computer game shop. It was called: 'CHANGE YOUR LIFE' and on the cover in red letters were the words … 'Warning: This game will lead to a happier, healthier life'.

Bailey stood up on his weak, shaky legs and walked towards the glass sliding door that opened out to the back garden. Through it, he could see his sister and his dad kicking the football to each other. He took a deep breath and opened the door to join them.

CHANGE YOUR LIFE! – 2

Use the text on page 79 to answer the questions.

❶ Literal

(a) Order the events from 1 to 5.

☐ A monkey tries to attack Bailey.

☐ Bailey arrives home from school.

☐ A pillar is struck by a fiery boulder and explodes.

☐ Bailey drops the game controller.

☐ Bailey hides behind a boulder.

(b) What made Bailey jump and run in midair?

_____

_____

_____

_____

_____

❷ Deductive

(a) Do you think Bailey enjoyed school? **Yes** **No**
Copy the sentence from the text that tells you this.

_____

(b) Why do you think Bailey 'couldn't catch his breath to speak' after running away from the monkey?

_____

(c) Explain how Bailey's feelings towards his X-box™ changed during the story.

Beginning of story	**End of story**

❸ Evaluative

(a) List words and phrases to describe how you think the man who handed Bailey the 'Change your life' game feels about computer games.

_____

_____

_____

_____

(b) Do you think Bailey will keep his promise? Explain your answer.

_____

_____

_____

_____

CHANGE YOUR LIFE! – 3

Refer to the text on page 79 to help you with this activity.

Bailey did keep his promise to play more sport and spend less time playing computer games. When he was older, Bailey decided that other children should learn about his story, so he decided to write to the 'Better Health Film Company'.

1 Write a paragraph that summarises Bailey's story and explains how it affected his life.

....

....

....

....

....

....

2 The film company accepts Bailey's proposal to make the film *Change your life!* and designers create a storyboard of four of the main scenes in the film. Draw and write about these four scenes from the film.

Scene 1

Scene 2

Scene 3

Scene 4